P8-AUW-756

LIVINGSTON
FOUNDATION

THE
COOKBOOK

THE
COOKBOOK

ANA MARIA CANALES

GRAPHICS AND ILLUSTRATIONS BY
BETSY AND DAN YAZVAC

LIVINGSTON FOUNDATION • SAN DIEGO

Copyright © 1996 by Livingston Foundation

All rights reserved. No portion of this book may be reproduced mechanically, electronically, or by any other means, including photocopying without written permission of the publisher.

Library of Congress Cataloging-in-Publication Data
Canales, Ana Maria
The Cookbook / by Ana Maria Canales
p. cm.
Includes index
ISBN 0-9650866-0-7
I. Cookery, American. I. Title.

Graphics by Betsy & Dan Yazvac

Books are available at special discounts when purchased in bulk for resale as well as for fundraising or educational use. For details, contact Executive Director at:

Livingston Foundation
3232 Duke Street
San Diego, CA 92110
(619) 224-3515   FAX (619) 224-6253

Manufactured in United States of America

First printing November 1996

DEDICATION

To Julie Anne Wagner,

whose dedication and commitment to continuing the
work of the Livingston Foundation and its Medical Center
has made this book possible, and who has enriched the
quality of life of all those who participate in the ongoing
Livingston programs. Without Julie's encouragement we
would not have moved forward.

With love to Dr. Virginia, Julie's mother.

ACKNOWLEDGEMENTS

**LIVINGSTON FOUNDATION MEDICAL CENTER
EXECUTIVE DIRECTOR**
Patricia Huntley

NUTRITIONIST
Janet Zuckerman

CULINARY STAFF
Clemente Diaz
Jesus Esquivel

CONTENTS

INTRODUCTION

In 1949, almost fifty years ago, Dr. Virginia Livingston isolated a microorganism that she believed to be a cancer-causing agent. Like many medical and scientific discoveries, this one came about by accident. But when she went on to experiment with laboratory animals, inoculating them with the organism, they developed cancer; further, identical acid-fast microbes in tumors she collected from nearby hospitals, when cultivated and injected into laboratory animals, led to evidence of cancer cells.

Dr. Livingston, always known as "Dr. Virginia", and her colleagues at the New York Academy of Sciences gave the orgainism its bacteriological classification, Progenitor Cryptocides (we refer to it as the PC microbe). And Dr. Virginia devoted the rest of her life to investigating the characteristics of the PC microbe. These investigations, in New York and in Southern California, convinced her that the correct diet plays an invaluable part in building a strong, disease-resistant immune system.

At the Livingston Foundation Medical Center, the immune-boosting diet developed by Dr. Virginia is a major component in our treatment of immunodeficiency diseases. We--and, to be sure, others--continue to investigate the changing world of good health and to advocate nutrition-based resistance to disease.

In continuing Dr. Virginia's work, and through supportive and caring relationships with our patients at the Center, we have come to realize that a healthy, nutritious, immune-boosting diet requires some effort to achieve. It requires, in more or less equal parts, some research and understanding, some sacrifice, some extra effort, some discretionary shopping practices, some shedding of old habits and acquiring of new ones -- that is, a general readjustment of our nutritional lifestyle.

Generally speaking, foods bought from the supermarket shelves of America today -- fruits and vegetables, for the most part -- do not have the same vitamin and mineral strength as they did when they sprouted from the ground or were picked from the tree.

Dr. Virginia often cited Emanuel Cheraskin, M.D., D.D.S., of the University of Alabama School of Medicine, whose thesis was that "from the garden to the gullet", the food on your table has lost at least half of its nutrients. This is because the mineral content of most America's arable soil has been reduced, most notably by pesticides and chemicals (10 percent), and because foods must be transported great distances today for consumption (10 percent). In fact, one study showed that a carrot eaten by an American today has far fewer nutrients in it than a carrot eaten by his Third World counterpart, simply because the latter probably got the carrot less than a mile from his home, whereas the more affluent American had his shipped from hundreds, even thousands, of miles away.

Dr. Cheraskin's analysis now leaves us with 80 percent. Storage in warehouses and supermarket shelves robs another 10 percent of nutrients, and freezing or premature harvesting takes another 10 percent. Washing and scrubbing in preparation for cooking, 5 percent. Now consider the way most Americans prepare their food, by boiling, broiling, baking, and frying. Broccoli and spinach, for example, are usually boiled to death, removing 50 percent of the nutrients in these potentially strong immunity-boosting vegetables. Meat gets overcooked, potatoes boiled to mush -- now you have about 40 percent of the original nutrients on your plate. After considering preservatives (to keep those bugs off the fruit), additives (to make those beets redder), processing (cheese), sweeteners (like the sugar added to catsup), and on and on, your plateful of dinner may be only at 30 percent of the nutritional power Nature intended for it.

We at the Livinston Foundation believe only a nutritionally informed person can hope to avoid the dietary pitfalls of daily life. In our present society we have the knowledge and skill to avoid or minimize the damages from immunodeficiency diseases with nutritionally powerful diets. There are simple things provided by Nature that we can use to prevent disease, alleviate ill health and prolong life. These "simple things" are our life habits, which include avoiding noxious substances such as alcohol and tobacco and working to avoid or control stress in our lives. Most importantly, we can become educated in the simple principles of good nutrition. In a society commercially oriented to the mass production of cheap food, preservatives to prolong shelf life, exploitation of taste over quality, convenience, attractive packaging, and the hustle-bustle of everyday working life, the trusting and unsuspecting individual can become lost in a jungle of incomprehension, leading to poor health and general deterioration.

When faced with a life-threatening disease such as cancer, most people are willing to comply with any program that might prolong life. We have all long known the value of Vitamin C in preventing scurvy and of the B vitamins in fighting pellagra. In the few years since Dr. Virginia's death, in 1990, new evidence has shown betacarotene has disease-resistant characteristics. How many of us know what other factors can increase the restorative functions of the body when faced with serious disease?

**LIVINGSTON
FOUNDATION**

We at the Livingston Foundation Medical Center have made certain recommendations to the patient with chronic debilitating diseases such as arthritis, cancer, or any other disabling collagen disease. In particular, we constantly strive to increase the immune potential of the cancer patient through research on nutrition. Based largely on Dr. Virginia's rather stringent original "anti-cancer diet," but modified over the years to accommodate the average person's lifestyle, we have developed a basic food guideline for all of us, healthy or ill, who desire stronger immunity-boosting benefits from their diets.

The guideline has certain outright prohibitions, such as the avoidance of cancer-infected food, refined flour, white sugar, and empty calories devoid of vitamins and minerals. In their place, we have prescribed food rich in minerals and vitamins and high in healing, nutritive substances. We have tried to present food that is palatable; adapted to the digestive capabilities of the sick; readily available; inexpensive; and easy to prepare.

This diet regimen is not intended as a treatment for cancer. It is intended to raise immunity and to increase the resistance of the patient to disease.

In addition to providing supplemental vitamins and minerals, we present natural sources of protective foodstuffs. We know that: Vitamin A guards against chemical carcinogenesis; vitamin C promotes healing; nicotinamide, B12, and riboflavin increase cellular oxidation; and abscisic acid, an analog of vitamin A, neutralizes human choriogonadotropin (HCG), a hormone that Dr. Virginia found promotes the growth of cancer cells.

Abscisic acid, a little-known derivative of Vitamin A, is a key component of the Livingston Foundation Diet. Almost a half-century ago, Dr. Virginia determined that the abscisic acid component of Vitamin A appeared to neutralize HCG. The actual chemical reaction is highly complex, but abscisic acid's importance to the immune system is the reason foods highly concentrated in Vitamin A are frequently emphasized in this cookbook.

Finally, a short word about vegetarianism and the general proscription against meat in these recipes.

Vegetarianism has been defined as either "scientific" (or "medical") vegetarianism or "emotional" vegetarianism. Emotional vegetarians are offended by the killing of animals by human beings, or their treatment while alive, or the idea of "predigested" flesh. These vegetarians often state that they won't eat anything "that has a mother," or that "has a face." Their passion is very real.

Dr. Virginia advocated "scientific" vegetarianism, that is, the eating of the healthiest food one can find, and eschewing all food, including meat, that is known to be infected by one substance or another, and which therefore likely harbors the PC microbe in its tissues.

Her early scientific work in the discovery of the PC microbe, her later medical work at Sloan-Kettering in New York City, and at her clinic in San Diego, California, overshadowed Dr. Virginia's deserved place as a pioneer in the nutrition movement in this country. While Adele Davis, et al., were calling attention to the benefits of vegetarianism (and being ridiculed for it by the meat industry and many other special interests), Dr. Virginia was quietly advocating the avoidance of what she called "contaminated" foods. One of these foods was chicken, which had been found almost universally to be infected with the PC microbe.

The basis of Dr. Virginia's recommendations against meat was not so much the meat, *per se*, as what happens to it on the way to your table. Just as with the "garden to the gullet" deterioration of fruits and vegetables, most meat has been largely "denatured" by the time it reaches your dinner plate. The unhealthy conditions of raising cattle, including the fertilizers and pesticides in their food, contribute in a major way to creating herds of unhealthy animals. Steroids are used to hasten their rate of growth. Many nutritionists believe that children are maturing faster these days -- such as earlier onset of menses -- because of the steroids in their diets.

Butchering techniques may not be properly selective, so that sick animals are often processed along with the healthy ones. While visible tumors are removed, animals remain systemically infected, and they are thrown into the process. The mass processing of cattle is simply too fast these days to adequately filter out unhealthy animals. Dr. Virginia believed that when *part* of a body is sick, such as a tumor or other organic infection, the *whole* body is sick. Hence, the whole animal should be removed from the process, not just the animal's tumor or infected part.

In many cases, when a patient cannot tolerate a strictly vegetarian diet, modifications can be made to include "cleaner" meat, such as lamb, wild game and fish. These foods have been found to have low incidences of PC microbe infection.

The bottom line is whether one wants to play it safe or gamble: to select the healthiest foods available, or take a chance on foods that have a high probability of contamination. The foods you select should always be of the highest quality.

Everyone, whether well or sick, should have a practical, working knowledge of modern nutrition; and each of us must learn *how* to choose the foods necessary for good health. Dr. Virginia Livingston often quoted this from Thomas Parran, M.D., a former head of the U.S. Public Health Service: "We must all remember that no one becomes well-nourished by accident."

We offer you this guide, with the wish it will help you - (and perhaps your family) - to find good nutrition and good health.

The Cookbook is not presented as a substitute for good medical care, rather as an adjunct to recovery from serious illness that is life threatening. Many of the principles in this book can be used to great advantage to promote the continuation of good health and to prevent physical degeneration.

DIET:
THE KEY TO HEALTH

...and the key to a healthy diet is *balance*. Diets restricted to a preponderance of one kind of food can be dangerous because they are not well-balanced. Both the mind and the body require a *variety* of foods to maintain health. We know that missing nutrients in the diet can lead to disease. What we sometimes don't appreciate is that foods provide many of the same nutrients.

Foods can be categorized according to their nutrient similarities such as grains, vegetables, fruits, beans, nuts and seeds, etc. Although there are major similar nutrients among these groups, there are, however, varying differences among their micro-nutrients. Therefore, the goal is to eat a variety of foods within each group in order to assimilate more of the nutrients required by the body.

Foods also vary in their concentration of fats, carbohydrates, and protein, with many foods predominant in one or the other. These foods should be taken in proper proportions, because it is also important to watch our caloric intake. Fat, for example, is the most concentrated in calories, yielding 9 calories/gram. However, carbohydrates and protein only yield 4 calories/gram. Therefore, foods that have a high concentration of fat should be consumed in small amounts.

Carbohydrates provide the most available energy to the body. Since the body needs energy at all times, the proportion of carbohydrates in the diet should be large. Hence, lots of carbohydrates, little fat.

Your body needs protein for structure and rebuilding of tissues, including muscle, which is constantly being broken down and rebuilt. Protein is derived from a variety of "building blocks" called amino acids. The body's requirement for protein is only moderate, because an excess won't be stored in the body but will be converted to carbohydrates or stored as fat. Therefore, a good exercise regimen is recommended, to maintain the delicate balance between these three food elements. (This balance is sometimes referred to as "homeostasis.")

It would be nearly impossible to go to the store and buy a pound of carbohydrates, or a pint of fat, or a package of protein. You must get them in varying degrees from the food your eat. And since all foods contain little "bundles" of fat, carbohydrates, protein, vitamins, minerals, fiber, and water, the proper proportions of these components becomes very important if the body is to digest and utilize micro-nutrients in perfect balance.

It's been shown that, when components of these complete bundles are isolated, removed and concentrated (such as fat and sugar), then ingested, the body's balance is disturbed. This is because the body cannot efficiently process one component without the presence of others in specific proportions. When it is forced to try, the result is stress to both mind and body -- and ongoing stress leads to disease.

Ideally then, foods should be consumed in their complete bundles of components to help bring about and insure ongoing health. For example, vegetables, whole grains, beans and legumes, fruits, nuts, and seeds are completely "bundled" foods. The body can assimilate the micro-nutrients in these foods quite nicely. That is why these food groups are the main constituents in a strict and balanced vegetarian diet.

The following illustration shows these food groups proportionately stacked in a pyramid-type scheme for optimum balance, according to their composition of fat, carbohydrates and protein. Note that the base (or largest

percentage of the pyramid) is
devoted to carbohydrate-rich
foods; the mid-section includes foods with a slightly
higher proportion of fat
(such as fruits and nuts
and seeds), as well as
the more refined soy
products derived from
the whole soybean;
and the top of the
pyramid contains
the high-fat foods
(the smallest
percentage of
the pyramid).
In summary,
as long as
you eat a
variety

OILS
CREAM
BUTTER
DRESSINGS

FRUIT
SOY PRODUCTS
RAW NUTS & SEEDS

VEGETABLES

WHOLE GRAINS

BEANS & LEGUMES

of foods in the proper proportion, it is easy to maintain a
balanced vegetarian diet promoting optimum health
The Cookbook is your guideline to those proper proportions.

Here are some of Dr. Virginia's prescriptions for healthy
eating gleaned from her lifetime of dealing with immune
deficiency diseases.

1. Very ill people should consume large amounts of fresh
    juices and homemade soups. These tend to saturate the
    system with organically-combined minerals, vitamins and
    liver-oxidizing enzymes, which in turn detoxify the body.
    The exception to this suggestion is when nothing can be
    kept in the stomach except water, then grain waters
    are recommended.

2. Eat organically-grown, unsprayed and unfumigated fruits
    and vegetables when available, or grow them yourself.
    The soil is a great metabolizer. A home garden - replete

with compost, earth worms and natural fertilizers -- is an ideal hobby for your dietary lifestyle. Conversely, wilted, pale, flabby, soft-spotted imperfect fruits and vegetables rob you of vitality and immune-building nutrients.

3. Increase your intake of high-potassium foods, such as greens, potatoes, lima beans, nuts and most fruits and vegetables. Try to combine legumes, grains, and leafy vegetables in planning your individual meals.

4. Decrease the high-sodium foods, such as celery and processed salted foods.

5. Learn to substitute:
    - arrowroot for thickening
    - yeast or egg replacer for leavening instead of eggs
    - oil and butter for shortenings
    - soy milk or whipping cream for milk
    - low-sodium baking powder, kelp, vegetable herb seasoning or sea salt for iodized salt

6. Add nuts to any recipe to increase the protein content.

7. Limit yourself to one or two pieces of citrus fruit per day and eat them whole, except for the skin.

8. Carry around a "snack bag" of carrot sticks, broccoli and other raw vegetables, nuts and dried foods.

9. Avoid refined or processed foods, because they are usually robbed of their nutrients. The less refined and more primitive the food stuff, the better.

10. Do not use any milk products, except cream and butter in moderate amounts. Products such as milk, cheese or yogurt contain the hormone prolactin, which stimulates unhealthy cell growth.

11. Bottled water is recommended for drinking and cooking

because most municipal water is fluoridated at the plant before it's even transported to your kitchen. Fluorine is a cumulative enzyme poison which is concentrated by cooking. Also, other unhealthy micro-organisms are often present in tap water.

12. Food should be cooked in stainless steel cookware, iron stone steamers or stainless steel steaming baskets. Avoid the use of pressure cookers, microwave ovens, aluminum pots and utensils.

13. Become a label detective. Read ALL labels. It's difficult, but try to avoid artificial colors, flavors, preservatives and sugar substitutes. Watch out for preservatives such as BHT and BHA. Read labels on products used for sweetening to make sure they contain no artificial sweeteners.

14. Alcoholic beverages, even wine, are not good for sick people. The same is true of soft drinks and iced drinks, because they inhibit digestion.

15. Quit smoking and avoid smoke-filled rooms.

16. Get at least eight hours of sleep, plus regular relaxation periods. Exercise daily according to your ability, and if possible, outside. Take hot baths daily to increase circulation. Cultivate a positive mental attitude.

Re-stock Your Pantry!

As you read the recipes and comprehend the general tone of *The Cookbook*, you'll begin to alter your shopping habits. Your pantry will take on a totally new look, and these are the foods that should eventually be stocked there.

Beverages: Herb teas, sesame or nut milk, soy milk, cereal coffee, dandelion or chicory teas.

Breads: Millet, rye, buckwheat, whole wheat, bran, corn, 7-grains, corn tortillas. Only whole grains-- freshly ground and free of all preservatives. No sprouted grain bread (the abscisins are lost).

Cereals: Millet, oatmeal, brown and wild rice, buckwheat, groats, barley, cornmeal, cracked wheat and 7-grain. Freshly ground rolled flakes or whole grain only.

Cheese: Only as directed. Generally not used.

Dairy: Heavy cream and butter in moderation.

Desserts: Fresh, whole fruits. Fresh fruit cocktails. Natural fruit gelatin. Healthy desserts and snacks made from outlined ingredients.

Eggs: Inoculated eggs from San Pasqual Farms. San Pasqual Farms eggs are now available at health food stores.

Fat: Olive oil, sesame oil, flaxseed oil and butter (raw if possible).

Fish: Freshwater and deep sea fish. Broiled, baked or poached.

Fruits: All fresh fruits, organically grown if possible. Use limited amounts of dried, unsulphured fruit as the sugars are very concentrated. The following are particularly high in abscisic acid: mango, pears, grapes, strawberries, apples (whole with the seeds), oranges with the white underpeel and pulp.

Juice: Only freshly pressed juices and frozen pineapple juice. The pressed juices may be selected from the list of fruits and vegetables listed in the introduction to *Beverages* section. Apple and carrot are the most popular. Include mature beet leaves, chicory, escarole, Swiss chard, watercress, beets, cucumber.

Meat: Lamb and its internal organs. Wild game such as venison may be consumed in small amounts by healthy people.

Nuts: Fresh, raw nuts, particularly walnuts, almonds, cashews, pecans and peanuts. Raw nut butters, freshly made in the blender or juicer only.

Salads: Use raw fruits and mature vegetables.

Sea Salt: Permitted.

Seasoning: All fresh herbs. Organically grown dried herbs when fresh is not available. Tamari, soy sauce and mustards. Lemon juice, vegetable bouillon, sea salt and kelp.

Seeds: Sunflower, chia, sesame, flaxseed, and pumpkin - fresh and raw.

Soups: Homemade soups.

Sweets: Natural sweeteners in moderation.

Vegetables: Organically grown: raw or freshly cooked. The following are particularly high in abscisic acid: avocados, asparagus, lima beans, pea shoots, peas, onions, tomatoes, all root vegetables especially carrots, potatoes, yams,and sweet potatoes. All mature leafy greens, especially spinach, Swiss chard, beet greens.

FOODS TO AVOID

Naturally, there is a long list of proscribed foods, which are either nutritionally deficient, or cancer-infected, according to Dr. Virginia's theories about the P. *Cryptocides* organism that causes cancer. In any case, these foods are downright bad for you.

Beverages: Alcohol, cocoa, coffee, soft drinks.

Bread: White bread and blended breads made out of white flour. Sprouted grain breads.

Cereals: Processed cereals which are puffed, and sugared. White rice.

Cheese: Only as directed. Generally not used.

Dairy: All milk products except as directed.

Desserts: Canned or frozen fruits. All pastries, gelatins, custards, sauces, ice cream, candy, except those made of suggested health ingredients.

Eggs: Forbidden in any form unless inoculated.

Fat: Shortening, margarine, saturated oils and fats. Rancid and continuously heated oils.

Fish: Smoked and salted fish. Fish preserved in antibiotics. Shell fish.

Fruits: Sprayed and sulfured. Canned and frozen.

Juices: All canned and frozen juices, except frozen pineapple juice.

Meats: Poultry, beef, pork in any form. Fatty meats such as bacon, ham, or ribs. No fried, smoked, salted or processed meats such as sausages and cold cuts. Veal.

Nuts: Salted nuts.

Potatoes: French fried, potato chips.

Sweets: White sugar and white sugar products such as candy, all sugar substitutes, and honey except as directed.

Vegetables: Sprayed, canned. Sulphur and high sodium foods. Frozen vegetables preferable to canned when fresh not available.

VITAMINS

The lively debate about the value of vitamins continues to rage throughout the scientific community. We know that some vitamins have value in preventing deficiency diseases like scurvy (Vitamin C) and rickets (Vitamin D), but only recently have some scientists admitted that vitamins may play a role in promoting optimum health and vitality. Regardless, it seems that with every new study, the medical community as a whole comes a tiny step closer to subscribing to the value of vitamins.

Dr. Virginia believed passionately in the immune-boosting value of some vitamins, the cancer-fighting value of others, and the optimum health value of still others. In fact, her multimodal immunotherapy treatment of cancer patients included large daily doses of specific vitamins. In particular, she believed in the cancer-fighting value of abscisic acid, an analog of Vitamin A, and in the immune-boosting value of Vitamin C, or ascorbic acid.

Readers of this book are encouraged to research for themselves the very latest scientific findings that corroborate many of Dr. Virginia's contentions. Here is a compact reference guide:

VITAMIN A

Vitamin A or retinol, a fat-soluble vitamin, has a special relationship to the epithelial tissues of the body including the skin, eyes, and the mucous membranes lining most of the organs of the body. It has a direct role in vision and is present in a pigment in the retina of the eye. Deficiency tends to create a rough and scaly skin, lack of saliva, easy tooth decay with defective enamel. A deficiency may also produce a dry cough or hoarseness, and a tendency to colds. Vitamin A deficiency may also cause muscular degeneration including the heart. Vitamin A malnutrition of the eyes impairs night vision and also makes daylight vision more difficult. Because of its relationship to the lining cells of the body, lack of it often causes inflammation of the delicate membranes which line the eyelids and cover the eyeball. Very often sores in the mouth, digestive system upsets, urinary tract diffuculities, glandular problems, and decreased stomach acid may all be traced to Vitamin A deficiency. There is a good supply of this vitamin in fruits, vegetables (especially the green and yellow ones), nuts, seeds, and fish liver oils. An excess of Vitamin A may be toxic, but cases of toxicosis are rare; Vitamin A toxicity can cause falling hair, nausea, and headaches. More often, however, and of far greater concern, is its deficiency.

VITAMIN A AND ABSCISIC ACID

Recent research has shown that Vitamin A is very protective against carcinogens, and lends credence to Dr. Virginia's theory that Vitamin A, which includes abscisic acid among it analogs can protect against cancer. The group of Vitamin A analogs are classified as retinoids, of which abscisic acid, a plant dormin, is a member. Abscisic acid appears to decrease the secretion of choriogonadatropic hormone (CGH) which is present in large amounts in tumor cells. Abscisic acid is present in seeds, nuts, grains, root vegetables, and mature leaves of plants and vegetables, but it decreases rapidly when seeds and nuts are soaked. It is also destroyed by heating to 250 degrees.

VITAMIN B1 (THIAMIN)

Vitamin B1 is valuable in the metabolism of carbohydrates and necessary for proper nerve function. Vitamin B1 deficiency can cause neuritis, irritability, insomnia, loss of appetite, abnormal heart action, poor circulation, enlarged heart, constipation and gas formation. Ordinary cooking does not destroy this vitamin, but adding soda to vegetables to make them look fresh does destroy Vitamin B1, as well as many others. Other indications of a deficiency of Vitamin B1 are nausea, vomiting, loss of appetite, headaches, general weakness, muscle cramps, sensation of burning in the feet, ear noises, difficult breathing. The richest sources available of Vitamin B1 are wheat germ, virgin yeast, whole wheat, peas and nuts.

VITAMIN B2 (RIBOFLAVIN)

Vitamin B2 is an important factor for growth and development. It is not stored in the body and is affected by light but not by air or heat. It helps to convert starches and sugars into energy. Often the first sign of deficiency is dimness of vision at a distance or in poor light. Other signs of deficiency are poor appetite, abdominal cramps, weight loss, dark red tongue, cracks in corners of the mouth, a pale, anemic appearance, and premature aging. This vitamin is not destroyed by heat but is destroyed by alkaline solutions, by addition of soda while cooking, or when exposed to strong light. Persons lacking this vitamin become sensitive to strong light. Good sources of this vitamin are green leafy vegetables, especially the outer leaves, which contain *five times* as much Vitamin B2 as the inner leaves. Other sources are beets, nuts, fruit, whole wheat bread, and fish.

NIACIN AND NIACINAMIDE

Niacin is one of the most important vitamins in alleviating schizophrenia and autism. This vitamin comes in two chemical forms, niacin and niacinamide. These have been extremely useful in treating moodiness, disorientation, lack of ability to concentrate, anxiety and irritability. Niacin often causes a flushing or tingling in the neck, forearms and hands soon after taking the vitamin but lasts only a few moments. However, non-flush tablets are just beginning to be manufactured. Niacinamide and niacin aid circulation and cell metabolism. The other B vitamins and Vitamin C need to be present for niacin to be most effective.

VITAMIN B6 (PYRIDOXINE)

Vitamin B6 has a soothing or sedative effect on the nerves. It is an important factor in preventing tooth decay. In animal experiments it has been learned that pyridoxine is necessary for proper functioning of the pancreas, especially in the insulin producing cells. Deficiency of this vitamin may result in oily skin, dizziness, nausea, fatigue, restlessness, stiffness of legs, trembling of limbs, a shuffling walk, and even anemia. The body needs magnesium to metabolize this vitamin. A form of iron-deficiency anemia can be brought on by inadequate amounts of Vitamin B6. Sources of this vitamin are available in corn oil, virgin yeast, honey, cabbage, whole grains, bread and fish.

VITAMIN B12 (CYANOCOBALAMIN)

Vitamin B12 is vital for blood-forming organs of the bone marrow, and is needed in the formation of hemoglobin. Cobalt and zinc are necessary for the body to produce it. Although it is absolutely necessary to make healthy blood, it takes only very small amounts to accomplish its function. Results of a deficiency can cause pernicious anemia. Other symptoms of deficiency are lack of nerve reflexes, a shuffling gait, loss of sense of the position of the feet. Insufficiency decreases production of sex hormones, retards development of the breasts, ovaries and other sex organs. In other words, females become less feminine and males less masculine. Sources of this vitamin are eggs, salt water fish, virgin yeast, wheat germ and soybeans. Meat contains more of this vitamin, hence vegetarians must insure an adequate supply, preferably by addition to their usual food intake.

VITAMIN C

Vitamin C is important in the synthesis of intercellular cement, or collagen, which supports and aids in the nourishment of every cell. The strengthening of collagen, as well as other supportive tissues of the body prevents the spread of bacteria, viruses, and other infectious elements from one cell to another, keeping them from penetrating the cell. It is in this sense that Vitamin C is considered a strong immune-boosting nutrient. While a healthy adult may need no more than 500 to 1,000 mg. daily, the amount to protect against disease, and especially its spread, can be many times greater. Some revered scientists recommend 1,000 mg. hourly for some diseased conditions. Biochemists Irwin Stone, Ph. D., and Linus Pauling, a Nobel laureate believe a *healthy* adult needs at least 5,000 mg. per day. Deficiency may cause bleeding gums, easy bruising, susceptibility to all kinds of infections. In severe cases of deficiency, scurvy occurs, as well as marked loss of energy, pain in the limbs and joints, loosening of teeth and easy bleeding. Vitamin C is high in ripe citrus fruits, but is also present in many fresh vegetables. There is often not enough in one's diet to supply the amounts needed for prevention of diseases such as the common cold. Take ascorbic acid to bowel tolerance in order to determine the level best for you -- i.e., when your bowels begin to loosen, scale back your dosage until you reach a comfortable level.

VITAMIN D

Vitamin D promotes bone and tooth development and regulates the absorption and fixation of calcium and phosphorus. It is not affected by heat or oxidation. It is synthesized in the skin by activity of ultraviolet light. Vitamin D is a factor in tissue cell respiration and is essential to maintain a normal basal metabolism. A deficiency of this vitamin produces rickets but can also cause restlessness, general soreness of the muscles, enlargement of liver and spleen, and may diseases caused by softening of bones both in infancy and in the aged. Its main source is fish oils. 2.500 to 5,000 International Units are considered to be the average amount needed daily. It is difficult to overdose when natural oils are used.

VITAMIN E (TOCOPHEROL)

There are actually five forms of Vitamin E, comprising a complex group, but they all act together as one vitamin. This vitamin is needed to maintain normal membranes of red blood cells. It is considered vital for the proper development and functioning of the reproductive organs, and its absence can cause sterility. It supplies oxygen to cells. Much has been written about Vitamin E and its value in preventing arteriosclerosis and heart disease. It accelerates healing of body tissues that have been infected or injured. Its tissue-building power is well authenticated. Bed sores or pressure sores that will not respond to any other methods, heal rapidly with the use of Vitamin E. Food sources are various plant oils. Its presence in smaller amounts is found in lettuce, brown rice, whole grain cereals, green vegetables, nuts and legumes.

VITAMIN F

Vitamin F consists of the unsaturated fatty acids. These fatty acids offer the most concentrated form of energy to the body. Unsaturated fatty acids combine with phosphorus to form a part of every cell and are particularly concentrated in nerve and brain tissues. These acids prevent high cholesterol build-up in the arteries. Some of the symptoms of lack of unsaturated fatty acids include emaciation, severe skin rashes, kidney disorders, difficulty in healing of even small wounds, interference with the ability to reproduce and shortening of the life span. Good sources of this vitamin are present in all oils, cream, nuts and avocados.

VITAMIN K

Vitamin K is essential for adequate blood clotting to prevent hemorrhages from even small cuts or wounds. Other symptoms can be dark urine, loss of appetite, general itching, slow pulse, and even jaundice. It is an excellent preventive of the tendency to bleeding caused by aspirin. Leafy vegetables are the most common source of this vitamin. It is also synthesized in the intestines by certain bacteria. It is present in fats, oats, wheat, rye, and alfalfa.

VITAMIN P (BIOFLAVINOIDS)

Vitamin P, also known as citron, is similar to Vitamin C in its general action. While whole Vitamin C acts mainly on the intercellular cement that binds cells together, Vitamin P has its main effect in strengthening the walls of the capillaries, thus preventing tissue fluids from seeping through into the surrounding cells. The interesting reason for the selection of the letter "P" to designate this vitamin was the word "permeable." It was discovered that this substance stabilizes the permeability of blood vessels. The main food source of this vitamin is natural vegetable juices and whole lemon.

CHOLINE

This is one of the B-complex vitamins. It is essential for proper functioning of the liver. *Chole* is the Greek word for "bile," which explains its name. Although synthesized in the body, it is not made in sufficient amounts to meet the need of man. It must therefore be supplied in food. It is essential for growth and for the prevention of fatty livers. It aids in the normal functioning of nerves and the synthesis of some proteins. Results of deficiency may be fatty liver, poor growth, edema, impaired cardio-vascular system, and hemorrhagic conditions in the kidney, heart muscle and adrenal glands. It is found in whole grains, legumes, wheat germ, and in small amounts in vegetables, but most other foods (except flesh foods) have little or no choline.

PANTOTHENIC ACID

Pantothenic Acid is needed for the proper functioning of the entire digestive system, especially the adrenal glands, and is essential for growth. Food processing has removed this vitamin from most food products on the store shelves. There is good reason to believe that a deficiency of this vitamin is a factor in promoting arthritis, gray hair, skin diseases, granulation of the eyelids, digestive disorders and mental depression. Children born of a mother deficient in Pantothenic Acid may be seriously deformed or mentally retarded.

This substance is found in royal jelly honey, human milk, wheat bran, virgin yeast, broccoli, molasses, peanuts, and nearly all vegetables.

NOTE:

This very brief summary of the role of vitamins in diet is intended only as an incentive to study in depth the elements essential for life in our daily food. The reader is also encouraged to study the role of minerals in the diet, although there are excellent multiple mineral supplements available that will complement the recipes in this book.

BEVERAGES

BEVERAGES

Juices, Herb Teas, Grain Waters, Nut and Seed Milks

Dr. Livingston always said, *"The very ill need juices primarily,"* This is because when you drink vegetable juice, you are consuming many times the concentration of that vegetable than you ordinarily would with a conventional diet, hence much more micronutrients per unit volume ingested. In other words, to get the nutrients from drinking a few ounces of, say, spinach juice, you would probably have to eat two pounds of spinach.

So we begin with this important form of nourishment: the raw beverage of vegetables.

It is extremely important that you buy the best quality of naturally grown produce you can find. Drinking juiced fruits and vegetables can be a double-edged sword. On the one hand, you are multiplying the nutritional benefits of the produce by the increased consumption of their juices; on the other hand, if you make juice from commercially grown or pesticide-sprayed produce, harmful toxins may also be concentrated in the juice. For this reason, it is also imperative that you wash your fruits and vegetables carefully, scrubbing them with a vegetable brush.

Dr. Virginia always suggested that juices be drunk without the addition of water so that the water in the diet wouldn't displace the juice. That is, less water = more room for the more nutritious juice. (Of course, you must drink water if no juice is available or if you are unable to keep juices down.)

Therefore, we recommend that you drink juices as often as you can. Because carrots contain a high concentration of abscisic acid, we specifically recommend drinking as much as a quart of carrot juice each day.

Here are some combinations for variety of taste:

Equal parts of carrot and apple juice
Equal parts of carrot and cucumber juice
Equal parts of carrot and fresh tomato juice
Equal parts of apple and grape juice (unsweetened)
3 parts of carrot juice to 1 part of spinach juice
3 parts of carrot juice to 1 part cabbage juice
4 parts of carrot juice to 2 parts cucumber juice and
    1 part beet juice

All juices should be prepared fresh and consumed within 1 hour of preparation, when possible.

The Foundation also recommends you use a *triturator* type of juicer. "Trituration" is a fancy word for pulverizing or crushing. At the Livingston Foundation Medical Center we use the Champion Juicer, one of the best kinds of triturators, because it efficiently macerates the fruits and vegetables with the least amount of oxygenation. We do not recommend centrifugal juicers, as they oxidize the food too much. Juicers may be purchased through the Center.

Finally, we have found that grain waters are easily assimilated and digested, and they provide excellent gastrointestinal relief. In all these recipes, you can add a tablespoon of freshly ground whole grain to any juice to neutralize tartness. Always use purified drinking water for teas and grain waters. Purified water will prevent the taste from being altered by chemicals or minerals in tap water.

PINEAPPLE CARROT JUICE

1   cup freshly squeezed carrot juice
½   cup fresh pineapple, cut in cubes

1. Blend in blender until smooth. Serve immediately.

APPLE CARROT JUICE

1   cup fresh apple juice
1   cup freshly squeezed carrot juice

1. Mix together and serve immediately.

CRANBERRY APPLE FRAPPÉ

½   cup frozen cranberries
2   cups fresh apple juice

1. Blend together in blender and serve.

PINEAPPLE PICK ME UP

1½   cups fresh pineapple juice
2   carrots, scrubbed well
      and chopped
1   medium stalk of celery
½   small apple, cored
      and chopped

1. Blend ingredients thoroughly in blender and serve.

GRAPE SUNSET

1   cup fresh grape juice
1   cup cranberry juice

1. Mix together and serve immediately.

MELON SEED DRINK

1   cup melon seeds and stringy center of melon
1   cup fresh pineapple juice

1. Place in blender and blend well until seeds are pulverized. Allow to sit for 5 minutes so pineapple enzymes can begin to digest seeds.

2. Strain and serve.

STRAWBERRY DELIGHT

1   cup strawberries
½   cup fresh pineapple, cut in chunks
1   medium apple, cored and sliced

1. Blend well or juice in juicer. Serve immediately.

CITRUS, CITRUS, & STRAWBERRY

½   grapefruit, pink or red
1   medium orange
1   cup strawberries

1. Hull strawberries and discard greens. Juice grapefruit & orange.

2. Blend with strawberries. Serve immediately.

TROPICAL SMOOTHIE

1	banana, cut in pieces
½	cup papaya, cut in pieces
½	cup strawberries, hulled
1	cup fresh pineapple juice

1. Blend together in blender until smooth.

SUMMERTIME SPECIAL

1	medium banana, frozen
1	large peach, peeled and pitted
1	cup cherries, pitted
1	cup fresh apple juice

1. Blend together in blender until smooth. Serve immediately.

BERRY, BERRY SPECIAL

2	medium pears
½	cup frozen blueberries
½	cup strawberries
½	cup apple juice

1. Juice pears. Combine with other ingredients in blender. Blend for 2 minutes. Serve.

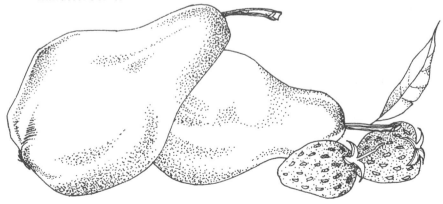

MANGO SPLASH

2	large mangoes, peeled and diced
1/2	medium banana
1/2	cup cranberry juice
1/2	cup orange juice

1. Blend ingredients together in blender. Serve immediately.

CARROT BEET UP

1/2	cup carrot juice
1/2	cup beet juice
1/2	potato juice

1. Make sure all juices are freshly squeezed.
   Mix together well. Serve immediately.

VERY VEGGIE JUICE

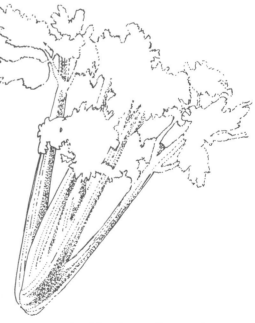

1	cup drinking water
1	carrot, sliced
1	stalk celery, cut in pieces
1	tomato, quartered
1/4	small onion, chopped
1/4	small jicama, cut in 1" pieces
1/2	medium cucumber, cut in 1" pieces
1	tbsp. apple cider
1	small clove of garlic
1/2	tsp. sea salt
1	tsp. Spike
1	tbsp. lemon juice

1. Blend all ingredients together at high speed in blender until smooth.
   More water may be added for thinner consistency.

TROPICAL BLAST

1   cup Red Zinger tea
1   cup frozen fruit (such as berries, peaches, pineapple, papaya, etc.)
1   small banana
1   pinch cayenne pepper

1. Blend all ingredients until smooth. Serve immediately.

SPICED APPLE CIDER

1   quart apple cider
½   cup pineapple juice
½   cup lemon juice
1   tsp. cinnamon
½   tsp. cloves, ground
½   orange, sliced & cut in half

1. Place in crock pot or on stove over medium heat in a non-corrosive pan to heat thoroughly. Serve hot.

VEGGIE JUICE

7   medium carrots
½   small beet
1   stalk celery
1   medium apple
1   cup green tops (such as beet)
1   clove garlic

1. Juice all ingredients in juicer. Serve immediately.

C.D.'s Herbal Iced Tea

4½   cups drinking water
1   tea bag each of: Red Zinger, Lemon Mist,
     Peppermint & Orange Zipper
1½   cups fresh apple juice

1. Bring 2½ cups of water to a boil. Add tea bags. Steep 6-9 minutes.

2. Stir in apple juice. Add remaining 2 cups of cold water and chill.

Mint Tea

1   tsp. mint
1   cup boiling water

1. Infuse for 5 minutes and strain.

Papaya Mint Tea

1   tsp. papaya leaves, dried
1   tsp. mint
2   cups boiling water

1. Infuse for 5 minutes and strain.

NOTES

PEACH BLOSSOM TEA

1 tsp. peach blossoms
1 cup boiling water

1. Infuse for 5 minutes and strain.

LEMON TEA

1 tsp. lemon grass tea
1 tsp. lemon balm tea
1 tsp. lemon verbena tea
1 tsp. citrus blossom tea
  or fresh citrus blossom
  such as orange or lemon
1 quart boiling water

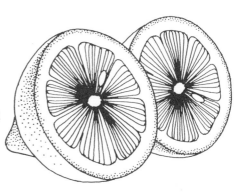

1. Infuse for 5 minutes and strain

ROSE HIP TEA

2 tsp. rose hips
2 cups water

1. Bring water to boil. Add rose hips. Cover and simmer for 15 minutes. Let cool. Strain.

GARDEN HERB TEA

½ cup garden fresh herb leaves
1 quart drinking water

1. Blend herbs with water. Allow to stand 20 minutes then strain.

FRESH GINGER TEA

1   1 inch piece fresh ginger root
1½ quarts drinking water

1. Grate root.
2. Steep in boiling water for 5 minutes, then strain.

FLAX TEA

1   tbsp. flax seed
1   cup drinking water

1. Grind seeds. Stir into water.
2. Bring to a simmer in a small sauce pan for 5 minutes. Strain.

RED CLOVER TEA

1½ tsp. red clover blossoms
1   cup drinking water

1. Pour boiling water over dried blossoms. Steep for 5 minutes. Strain.

GRAIN MEAL WATER

1   tbsp. any whole grain or mixture such as rye, rice, barley or millet
2   cups drinking water

1. Grind grain. Mix with cold water. Bring to boil in sauce pan. Lower heat and simmer for 1 hour.
2. Cool and serve. Do not store for over 5 days.

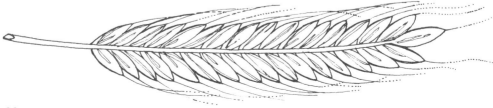

BARLEY WATER

2   **ounces whole barley**
3   **pints drinking water**

1. In a sauce pan boil barley and water until water is reduced by half. Strain. Cool. Do not store for more than 5 days.

RICE WATER

1   **tbsp. rice, ground in food mill**
2   **cups drinking water**

1. In medium sauce pan, mix rice with cold water. Bring to boil. Lower heat and cook for 5 minutes stirring constantly. Cool. Do not store for more than 5 days.

CORNMEAL WATER

1   **tbsp. freshly ground cornmeal**
2   **cups drinking water**

1. In medium sauce pan, mix corn and cold water. Bring to boil. Lower heat and simmer for 1 hour. Cool. Do not store for more than 5 days.

NOTES

WHEAT WATER

1   tbsp. whole wheat berries, freshly ground
2   cups drinking water

1. In a medium sauce pan, mix ground wheat with cold water. Bring to boil and simmer for 1 hour. Cool and Serve.

ALMOND MILK

2   cups drinking water
1   cup almonds
¼   cup apple juice (optional)
1   tsp. sea salt

1. Blend until smooth. Add more water or almonds to adjust to desired consistency. Apple juice sweetens the milk.

CASHEW MILK

2   cups drinking water
1   cup cashews
1   tsp. honey <u>OR</u> ¼ cup apple juice

1. Blend until smooth. Add more water or cashews to adjust to desired consistency.

SESAME MILK

2   cups drinking water
½   cup sesame seeds
2   dates, pitted and chopped

1. Blend all ingredients until smooth. Add more water or sesame seeds to adjust to desired consistency.

SUNFLOWER SEED MILK

2	cups drinking water
1	cup sunflower seeds
¼	tsp. sea salt
¼	tsp. pure vanilla extract
1	tbsp. currants (optional)

1. Blend until smooth. Add more water or sunflower seeds to adjust to desired consistency. Currants sweeten the milk.

SOY MILK

Choose a full-fat soy bean powder for making soy milk, rather than a de-fatted powder as the abscisic acid is in the fat part of the seed or bean.

1	part full-fat soy bean powder
4	parts drinking water

1. Mix soy bean powder with water. Let sit for 2 hours.
2. Mix again, then transfer to a double boiler to cook for 20 minutes.
3. Strain through a fine sieve and add one of the following for flavoring:

¼ cup carob powder	2 tsp. vanilla
1 cup apple juice	1 cup prune juice
1 cup papaya juice	1 cup carrot juice

APPLE ALMOND MILK

1½	cups apple juice
¼	cup almonds, ground and raw

1. Blend and chill for 20 minutes. Do not keep overnight.

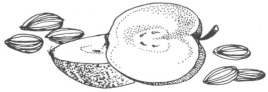

CARROT ALMOND MILK

½   cup raw almonds, ground
2   cups drinking water
2   cups carrot juice

1. Place ground nuts in blender with water and blend for 2 minutes.
2. Mix well with carrot juice. Drink immediately.

SESAME CREAM

½   cup raw sesame seeds
½   cup drinking water
½   cup carrot juice
¼   tsp. vanilla

1. Blend together sesame seeds and water until smooth. Add carrot juice and vanilla, just to blend.

OPTION: Substitute a banana for carrot juice

NUT CREAM

1   tbsp. raw cashews
1   tbsp. raw almonds
1   tbsp. raw sesame seeds
¾   cup drinking water
2   tbsp. coconut juice
¼   tsp. vanilla
½   tsp. raw honey

1. Grind nuts and seeds in blender until fine. At high speed add water until well combined.
2. Blend nut milk with other ingredients until smooth. Serve with breakfast cereals or fruit.

SESAME NUT CREAM

1	cup sesame milk
½	cup almond or cashew butter
2	dates, chopped and pitted

1. Blend all ingredients until smooth. Serve over fruits or salad.

PROTEIN SHAKE

½	cup fresh or frozen fruit
½	cup cooked grain (rice, millet, etc.)
1	cup drinking water
¼	cup cream OR ½ cup soy milk
2	tbsp. raw nuts or seeds
1	tbsp. flaxseed or safflower oil
1	tsp. amino acid powder
1	tsp. vanilla
1	tsp. barley malt sweetener (optional)
1	egg (optional)

1. Blend all ingredients in blender until smooth. Dilute with additional water if desired. Drink immediately.

NOTES

CAFE MOCHA

<u>TOPPING</u>:

½	cup cream
1	tsp. honey
½	tsp. cinnamon
⅛	tsp. nutmeg

<u>COFFEE</u>:

1 to 2	tsp. Kafree or other coffee substitute for each cup boiling drinking water
1	tsp. carob powder for each cup
4	cups drinking water, boiling

1. Whip cream with honey, cinnamon and nutmeg. Set aside.

2. Place 1-2 tsp. coffee substitute in each mug with 1 tsp. of carob powder. Add water and stir to mix thoroughly. Top each drink with cream topping and serve.

BREAKFAST
FOODS

BREAKFAST FOODS

CEREALS, PANCAKES, MUFFINS AND MUCH MORE

Breakfast is the most often forgotten meal for most Americans, yet we know that breakfast is crucial to maintaining good health as it is truly the meal in which we "break fast". We should not skip breakfast at all; simple healthful meals requiring little time to prepare should always be taken. When time allows, preparation of an expanded meal will always be appreciated by your newly awakened self!

Breakfast foods included in this section range from a one minute protein shake to hearty fares meant to offer substance throughout the day. You may find many of the recipes familiar, with substitutions made only to make the meal healthier. The egg replacer called for in recipes requiring eggs for baking must be a *non-dairy* one. This means that it comes in powdered form and is *not* made from egg whites. Baking powder used in any recipe must be of the *non-aluminum* variety. Tofu cheese comes in many flavors, and we find the Monterey Jack "melt cheese" works very well.

We have included a few of Dr. Virginia's personal favorite egg recipes, including the Medical Center's "Eggs Benedict" for those who are fortunate enough to have inoculated eggs available to them.

As you study the recipes, you will notice that cream mixed with water often replaces traditional amounts of milk called for in a recipe. Don't worry about the amount of cream, because it is not based on an individual serving but rather the entire recipe. Some recipes call for honey, which used in moderation is not unhealthy. However, feel free to substitute apple or pineapple juice if a no-sugar diet has been recommended by your physician.

Most of the recipes include fruits, vegetables, nuts and seeds, because Dr. Virginia always felt the day should begin with concentrated amounts of vitamins and minerals from fruits and vegetables and the protein from nuts and seeds. Always have fresh juice with your breakfast entree.

FRUIT NUT GRANOLA

3	cups rolled oats
1	cup wheat flakes
1	cup rye flakes
1	cup bran
1	cup dried apples, chopped
½	cup dates, chopped
½	cup golden raisins
¼	cup dried apricots, chopped
¼	cup dried bananas
½	cup cashews, chopped
¼	cup raw sunflower seeds
½	cup raw honey
½	cup hot water
1	tbsp. pure vanilla extract

1. Combine all dry ingredients, fruits and nuts in a large bowl.

2. In a small mixing bowl, combine honey, hot water and vanilla. Add to dry ingredients. Mix thoroughly using your hands to coat all ingredients.

3. Spread on a baking sheet. Place in a 250° oven. Bake for 1 hour, stirring every 15 minutes or until golden brown.

4. Let mix cool completely. Store in tightly sealed container for up to two weeks.

Makes 9 cups

NOTES

TROPICAL MUESLI

3   cups rolled oats
¼   cup coconut, unsweetened
¼   cup pecans, chopped
¼   cup sliced almonds
¼   cup sunflower seeds
½   cup orange juice
¼   cup dried mango, finely chopped
¼   cup dried banana, finely chopped
¼   cup dried pineapple, finely chopped

1. Mix oats with coconut, nuts and seeds with orange juice. Place in a 250° oven. Bake for 45 minutes to 1 hour, stirring every 15 minutes or until coconut is lightly browned. Remove and cool completely.

2. Add chopped dried fruits to mix. Store in tightly covered container for up to two weeks.

3. To serve, place muesli in bowl, top with pineapple or orange juice. It is also delicious with nut milks.

Makes 5½ cups

OLD FASHIONED DUTCH CEREAL

1   cup barley flakes
2   inch cinnamon stick or ½ tsp. ground
1   lemon peel, 1" long
3   cups drinking water
1   cup unsweetened cranberry juice
½   cup golden raisins or currants
⅛   cup raw honey
2   tsp. sesame seeds

1. Cook barley flakes with cinnamon and lemon peel in water for 10 minutes. Add cranberry juice, raisins and honey. Cook 5 minutes more.

2. Remove cinnamon stick and lemon prior to serving. Top with sesame seeds and serve.

Serves 4

CREAMED KASHA WITH SEEDS AND FRUIT

1	cup Kasha (buckwheat groats)
4	cups water
1	tsp. sea salt
½	pint fresh or frozen berries
2	tbsp. raw honey
1	tbsp. lemon or lime juice
1	tsp. pure vanilla extract
½	cup sunflower seeds
½	cup golden raisins

1. Grind kasha in a blender or coffee mill. In a medium sauce pan, blend kasha with 1 cup water until smooth. Add remaining water and salt.

2. Bring to a simmer, stirring constantly. Cover and simmer for 15 minutes, stirring occasionally. Add more water as necessary.

3. While kasha cooks, puree berries in blender or food processor. Put pureed berries through sieve to remove seeds. Add honey, lemon juice and vanilla to taste. Set aside.

4. When kasha has finished cooking, add sunflower seeds and raisins. Serve in individual bowls with berry sauce on the side.

Serves 2

GROATS WITH SEEDS

3½	cups drinking water
½	cup apple juice
1	cup groats
½	tsp. nutmeg
1	tbsp. sesame seeds
1	tbsp. pumpkin seeds
1	tbsp. flax seeds
1	tbsp. cashews, finely chopped

1. In heavy sauce pan, bring water and apple juice to boil. Add groats and cook for 45 minutes. Stir in nutmeg, seeds and nuts. Top with seasonal fresh fruit.

Serves 4

Rancho Caliente Granola

5	cups rolled oats
¾	cup pecans, chopped or broken
¾	cup pumpkin seeds
¾	cup hulled sesame seeds
½	cup sesame or safflower oil
½	cup raw honey

1. Mix dry ingredients.
2. Mix oil and honey together. Add to dry ingredients, using hands to mix thoroughly.
3. Bake in a low oven, 250° for 1 hour or until golden. You must turn grains every 15 minutes to insure even color.
4. Let mix cool completely. Store in tightly sealed container for up to two weeks.

Makes 8 cups

Cashew Oat Waffles

2	cups rolled oats
⅓	cup raw cashews
2¼	cups water
1	tbsp. oil
½	tsp. salt

1. Combine all ingredients in blender. Blend until light and foamy. Let mixture stand while waffle iron is heating. It will thicken. Blend again briefly.
2. Bake in hot waffle iron for 8 to 10 minutes until nicely browned.

Makes 4 waffles

BANANA NUT PANCAKES

1   cup whole wheat pastry flour
2   tsp. baking powder (non-aluminum variety)
1¼   cup nut milk
2   tbsp. unsweetened apple sauce
1   medium firm but ripe banana, finely chopped
2   tbsp. cashews chopped

1. Mix flour and baking powder together.

2. Mix nut milk with applesauce. Add to dry ingredients. Stir until just moistened.

3. Fold in bananas and nuts.

4. Spoon batter on to lightly greased non-stick pan. When bubbles appear, turn gently to brown other side.

5. Serve with any combination of fresh fruit or fruit sauce.

Makes 10-12 4" pancakes

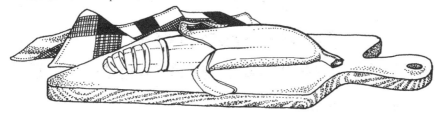

APPLE CAKES

1   cup cornmeal
½   cup garbanzo bean flour
1   tsp. cinnamon
1   cup apple juice
1   tbsp. raw honey
1   cup apple, scrubbed and grated

1. Mix together cornmeal, flour and cinnamon. Add apple juice and honey, stirring well. Fold in grated apples.

2. Spoon batter onto non-stick griddle. Cook for 3-5 minutes over medium heat until bubbles begin to appear. Turn once to brown other side.

Serves 6

BLUEBERRY PANCAKES

2	cups whole wheat pastry flour
1	tbsp. baking powder (non-aluminum variety)
2	cups water
¼	cup apple juice
½	tsp. lemon peel, grated
½	cup fresh, small blueberries

1. Mix flour and baking powder together. Add water and apple juice. Mix well. Gently fold in lemon peel and blueberries.

2. Spoon batter onto non-stick griddle. Cook for 3-5 over medium heat until bubbles begin to appear. Turn once to brown other side. Serve with whipping cream.

Makes 12 4" pancakes

SOURDOUGH BUCKWHEAT PANCAKES

1	tbsp. raw honey
1½	cups hot water
1	tsp. dry yeast
1½	cups buckwheat flour
1½	cups wheat berries (freshly ground)
1	tbsp. melted, unsalted butter
½	tsp. sea kelp or sea salt

1. Stir honey into water until dissolved. Add yeast and stir until dissolved. Let stand for 5 minutes.

2. Add remaining ingredients and beat well. Cover with a towel and let sit over night to develop sourdough flavor.

3. Drop by spoonful onto greased griddle. Cook until bubbles start to form. Gently turn and brown other side. Serve with applesauce.

Makes 14 4" pancakes

JOHNNY MEAL CAKES

1½	cups white water-ground cornmeal
6	tbsp. unsalted butter, 1 tbsp. softened, the rest sliced into pats
1	tsp. sea salt
1	tsp. molasses
1½	cups boiling water
1	tbsp. cream
¼	cup water
1	tsp. cinnamon (optional)

1. Place cornmeal, softened butter, salt and molasses in a large mixing bowl. Pour enough of the boiling water over these to form a stiff dough. Beat thoroughly and let mixture stand for 3-5 minutes to thicken.

2. Mix together cream and water with cinnamon. Use cream mixture to thin cornmeal batter to a consistency that will drop off the end of a spoon.

3. Heat greased griddle to hot. Drop dough by spoonfuls onto griddle. Reduce heat to low. Cook for 10-15 minutes, turning once to brown both sides.

4. Split johnny cakes and place a pat of butter between halves. Serve when butter is melted.

Makes 18 small cakes

QUICK MORNING SHAKE

1	cup strawberries
1	banana, sliced
1	cup papaya or pineapple
1	cup apple juice
8	oz. tofu
1	tbsp. wheat germ or brewer's yeast
1	tsp. raw honey
1	tsp. vanilla
½	tsp. ground ginger

1. Blend all in blender until smooth. Makes two shakes.

Serves 2

SIMPLE MUFFINS

2	cups whole wheat pastry flour
2	tsp. baking powder (non-aluminum)
½	tsp. sea salt
2	cups nut milk
2	tbsp. applesauce
½	tsp. vanilla

1. Combine dry ingredients. Combine wet ingredients. Fold together until just moistened. Spoon into lightly oiled or non-stick muffin tins.

2. Bake at 350° for 25-30 minutes.

Makes 12 muffins

CORN MUFFINS

1	cup cornmeal
1	cup soy flour
4	tsp. baking powder (non-aluminum)
1	tsp. cinnamon
½	tsp. nutmeg
½	tsp. allspice
½	tsp. sea salt
1⅔	cups warm water
2	tbsp. raw honey

1. Combine dry ingredients. Combine water and honey. Mix together until just moistened. Spoon into lightly greased or non-stick muffin tins.

2. Bake at 375° for 20 minutes.

Makes 12 muffins

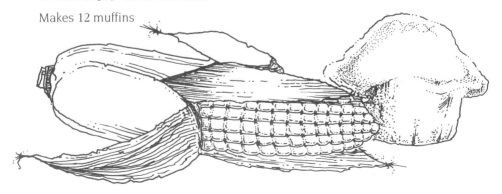

OATMEAL APPLE MUFFINS

1½   cups rolled oats
1   cup shredded raw apple
¼   cup apple juice
1   tsp. fresh lemon zest
¼   cup safflower oil
½   tsp. sea salt
½   cup currants
¼   cup nuts, chopped

1. Combine all ingredients. Let stand for 5 minutes to moisten all ingredients. Mix well.

2. Place in greased muffin cups. Bake at 375° for 25 minutes. Serve with unsalted butter and honey.

Makes 12 muffins

NOTES

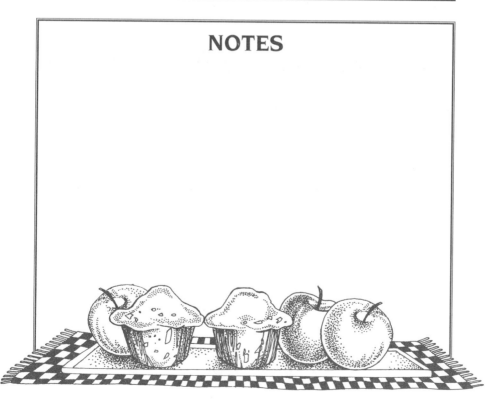

BRAN MUFFINS

1   tbsp. yeast

⅓   cup warm water

½   tsp. raw honey

1¼   cups nut milk, warmed

3   tbsp. apple sauce

1¼   cups whole wheat pastry flour

1   tsp. soy flour

1½   cups bran

½   cup currants or raisins

1. In small bowl, dissolve yeast in warm water and honey. Let sit 5 minutes.

2. In large mixing bowl, combine warmed nut milk with applesauce. Add yeast mixture. Stir in whole wheat and soy flours, ½ cup at a time. Gently stir in bran. Add currants. Fold gently.

3. Place batter into lightly greased or non-stick muffin tins, filling ⅔ full. Let rise in warm place for 30 minutes. Bake in preheated 325° oven for 25 minutes. Remove from muffin tins and set on rack to cool.

Makes 12 muffins

SWEET POTATO BISCUITS

2   cups whole wheat pastry flour

2   tbsp. baking powder

1   tsp. sea salt

10   tbsp. butter

1   medium sweet potato, peeled, boiled and mashed

1   tsp. fresh orange peel, grated

3   tbsp. cream

1. Mix flour, baking soda and salt. Cut in butter. Blend in sweet potatoes and orange peel. Add just enough cream to form a soft dough.

2. Turn dough onto lightly floured surface. Roll out to ¾" thick. Cut dough into squares or use a cookie cutter to cut rounds.

3. Bake in a preheated 400° oven for 15-20 minutes. Serve with sugar-free preserves.

Makes 12 biscuits

APRICOT AND STRAWBERRY DELIGHT

1	pint fresh strawberries
6	large ripe apricots
2	tbsp. fresh lemon juice
¼	cup raw honey
½	cup whipping cream
4	whole English muffins, toasted

1. Slice strawberries and apricots into medium sized bowl.

2. Pour lemon juice and ⅛ cup of honey over fruit. Toss gently to combine flavors. Set aside.

3. Whip cream in cold, clean mixing bowl. As cream thickens, slowly add remaining honey.

4. Place toasted muffins on individual plates, top with fruit and cream. Serve immediately.

Serves 2-4

PEAR BREAKFAST ROLLS

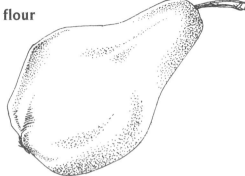

2   cups whole wheat pastry flour
½   tsp. baking soda
1   tsp. cream of tartar
¼   cup cream
¾   cup water
2   tbsp. honey
1½   cups fresh pears,
     peeled and finely diced
½   cup butter

1. Mix together flour, baking soda and cream of tartar in large mixing bowl. In small bowl, mix together cream, water and honey.

2. Add liquid mixture to dry ingredients. Mix well. Add pears.

3. Grease muffin cups with butter. Place a pat of butter in each cup. Heat muffin pan on top of stove until very hot. Fill cups ⅔ full with batter. Let stand for 1 minute.

4. Place in 425° oven for 12-15 minutes until browned.

Makes 18 rolls

FIG BREAKFAST BARS

3   tbsp. sesame seeds
½   cup almond butter
⅓   cup raw honey
4   tbsp. unsalted butter
2½   cups granola
3   tbsp. sunflower seeds
½   cup figs, finely chopped

1. Sprinkle sesame seeds over bottom of 8x8 baking pan.

2. Place almond butter, honey and butter in a small sauce pan. Cook over low heat 4-6 minutes until smooth and melted.

3. Mix almond butter mixture with granola, sunflower seeds and figs. Press into prepared pan. Allow to cool 1 hour before cutting into bars.

Makes 24 bars

Scrambled Tofu with Rice Cakes

2   tbsp. sesame oil
¼   cup yellow onions, finely chopped
14   oz. tofu
1   tbsp. Shoyu (natural soy sauce)
¼   cup parsley, finely chopped

1. Heat sesame oil in pan over medium heat. Add onions. Saute for 3-5 minutes until onions are translucent.

2. Crumble tofu into onion/oil mixture. Use a fork to scramble gently for 3-4 minutes until tofu is heated through. Add shoyu and parsley. Continue cooking for 3-4 more minutes.

3. Serve with rice cakes and any salsa of choice.

Serves 4

Spinach Omelet

¼   cup olive oil
1½   cups fresh spinach, chopped
1½   cups swiss chard leaves, chopped
1   clove garlic, peeled and mashed
8   inoculated eggs, well beaten
⅓   cup soy parmesan cheese
1   tbsp. parsley, finely chopped
1   tbsp. fresh basil, finely chopped
2   tbsp. butter

1. Heat oil in large skillet. Add spinach, chard and garlic. Cook mixture until oil is absorbed and leaves have wilted. Cool slightly. Add eggs, cheese, parsley and basil.

2. Heat butter in omelet pan. Pour in egg mixture. Cook over medium heat for 10-12 minutes to set omelet.

Serves 4

EGGS BENEDICT

<u>SAUCE:</u>

6	egg yolks (from inoculated - San Pasqual eggs)
1	tsp. lemon juice
⅛	tsp. cayenne
⅛	tsp. vegesal or sea salt
½	cup butter melted
2	whole wheat English muffins, split
4	slices ripe tomato
8	slices avocado
2	tsp. unsalted butter
4	inoculated eggs
3	tbsp. water

1. To make the sauce, place egg yolks, lemon juice, cayenne and vegesal in blender. Blend for 1 minute. Very slowly add the melted butter in a continuous stream until sauce thickens. Keep warm.

2. Toast muffins. Place a tomato slice on each muffin. Place 2 slices avocado on each half.

3. Melt butter in non-stick skillet. Add eggs and water. Cover. Cook 5-7 minutes until egg whites are solid and white. Place 1 egg on each muffin.

4. Pour warmed hollandaise sauce over each portion.

Serves 2

NOTES

WILD RICE SCRAMBLE

2	tbsp. butter
¼	cup celery, finely chopped
¼	cup green bell peppers, finely chopped
8	inoculated eggs
⅓	cup cream
1	cup cooked wild and brown rice
½	tsp. salt
½	tsp. black pepper

1. Heat butter in a large skillet. Saute celery and green peppers over medium heat until soft.

2. Lightly beat eggs with cream. Add wild rice. Pour egg mixture over vegetables in skillet. Scramble until eggs are set but still soft. Season with salt and pepper.

Serves 4

TOFU RANCHEROS

2	tbsp. corn oil
¼	cup green onions, chopped finely
¼	cup mild roasted chilies, chopped finely
¼	cup ripe tomatoes, chopped finely
1	tsp. cumin
½	tsp. sea salt
½	tsp. freshly ground pepper
14	oz. tofu
¼	cup fresh corn, cut from cob
¾	cup "Monterey Jack" tofu cheese, grated
6	whole wheat flour tortillas
6	lime wedges

1. Heat oil in oven-proof skillet over medium heat. Add onions. Saute 3-5 minutes until onions are soft. Add chilies, tomatoes and seasonings. Cook 3-5 minutes longer.

2. Crumble tofu into vegetable mixture. Cook for 3-5 minutes until heated through. Add fresh corn.

3. Top with grated "Monterey Jack" cheese. Place under broiler for 2-3 minutes to melt cheese. Serve with warmed tortillas, lime wedges and fresh salsa.

Serves 6

BLACK BEANS AND EGGS

2	tbsp. olive oil
½	cup onion, finely chopped
2	cloves garlic, peeled and mashed
2	15 ounce cans of black beans, drained and rinsed OR 3 cups cooked black beans
½	cup water
½	tsp. cumin
½	tsp. chili powder
1	cup tofu cheese
6	inoculated eggs
1½	cups fresh salsa
½	cup avocado diced

1. Heat oil in large sauce pan. Add onions and cook until translucent but not brown. Add garlic, beans, water and spices. Cook over low heat to combine flavors. Mash bean mixture well with a fork.

2. Add cheese to beans. Distribute the mixture among six buttered ramekins. Make a hollow center of each and slide an egg into each hollow. Bake in preheated oven at 350° for 15 minutes, until eggs are firm.

3. Remove ramekins from oven. Distribute salsa and avocados evenly over each and serve.

Serves 6

CHILAQUILLAS

1	dozen several day old tortillas
¼	cup safflower oil
½	cup green onions, sliced
2	tsp. chili powder
1	tsp. sea salt
½	tsp. dried oregano, crushed
1½	cups tomato sauce
8	ounces soy cheese

1. Tear tortillas into 2 inch pieces. Heat oil in large skillet. Add onions, cooking over medium heat until soft but not browned. Add chili powder, salt and oregano. Stir in tortilla pieces. Stir gently until all tortilla pieces are coated with oil.

2. Pour tomato sauce over tortillas. Top with grated cheese. Cover pan with lid and continue to heat over medium heat until cheese is melted and sauce is bubbly.

Serves 6-8

APRICOT CARROT BREAD

2	cups whole wheat pastry flour
1	cup stone-ground whole wheat flour
1	tbsp. baking powder (non-aluminum)
1	tsp. sea salt
1	tbsp. egg replacer
1	cup water
⅔	cup honey
⅓	cup cream
4	tbsp. unsalted butter, melted
1	tsp. fresh orange peel
1	cup carrots, scrubbed and grated
1	cup sulphur free, dried apricots, finely chopped

1. Mix together flours, baking powder and salt. Mix 2 tbsp. water with egg replacer in small bowl.

2. In a large bowl, beat egg replacer together with honey, remaining water, cream, butter and grated orange peel. Stir in carrots and apricots. Add flour mixture to blend thoroughly but gently with a spatula.

3. Divide batter between two 1 pound coffee cans. Cover tops with foil and secure with string. Place cans on trivet or canning rack in a large pot. Fill with boiling water until it reaches half way up can sides. Cover pot and simmer (do not let it boil) for 3 hours.

4. Remove cans from water. Remove covers, taking care to let steam escape away from your hands or body. Place cans in preheated 300° for 10 minutes to dry bread. Then, let sit on a rack for 5 minutes. Gently slide loaves out. Allow to cool on rack if not serving immediately.

Makes 2 1-pound loaves

NOTES

CORN BREAKFAST CAKE

TOPPING:

½	cup unsweetened coconut
½	cup raw apple, shredded
½	cup pecans, chopped
¼	cup raw honey
¼	cup unsalted butter, melted

CAKE:

1	cup cornmeal
1	cup soy flour
2	tsp. baking powder (non-aluminum)
1	tsp. cinnamon
½	tsp. nutmeg
½	tsp. allspice
½	tsp. sea salt
2	tbsp. unsalted butter, melted
1⅔	cup warm water
2	tbsp. raw honey

1. Combine all ingredients for topping in a small bowl. Set aside.

2. Combine dry ingredients. Combine water, butter and honey. Mix together until just moistened. Spoon into lightly oiled round cake pan. Top with fruit mixture.

3. Bake at 375° for 20 minutes.

Serves 6

NOTES

SANDWICHES

SANDWICHES
Spreads, Fillings and Whole Entities

Of all meal components, what can be considered more American than the sandwich? But the sandwich itself is not an American invention. In the introduction to her award-winning *Great Sandwiches*, Susan Costner reminds us that, although sandwiches were named for the England's Earl of Sandwich, who wanted a ready-made snack handy at his gaming tables, the sandwich reached its greatest height in America. Americans do seem to love the sandwich's convenience, as well as its connection to memories from childhood years.

Originating in all parts of America, these sandwich recipes are as varied and ethnic as the immigrants themselves who first adapted their traditional foodstuffs to the art of sandwich making. Of course, to taste its best, each sandwich relies on the freshest produce, the most healthful additions and hearty, whole wheat and multi-grain slabs of bread to hold them together.

Delicious, whole grain products are currently available in markets everywhere, making it a simple feat to create a delectable sandwich in no time.

Many of the sandwiches call for an eggless mayonnaise, which may be purchased at your supermarket. However, if you are lucky enough to be able to buy inoculated eggs, feel free to make your own San Pascual mayonnaise, following the recipe in the dressing section. We specify the eggless mayonnaise simply because it is ready-made, which seemed to follow the dictates of sandwich making -- *ease*.

Tofu cheese is available in many markets and almost all health food stores. For hot sandwiches, we prefer the "jack" style, which melts readily. Soy parmesan is also available for cheese flavor, and may be sprinkled liberally on any sandwich, because tofu is a great source of vegetable protein.

We hope that the basic ideas behind these sandwich recipes encourage you to experiment with your own variations. For example, spices have been chosen to enhance flavor to a maximum, but for those with timid palates or sensitive stomachs, you may wish to mix and match or to modify accordingly.

We think that you will find these recipes an enchanting challenge to midday eating in America's finest tradition.

BERINJELA EGGPLANT FILLING

1   small eggplant, baked until soft, then peeled and chopped
3   green olives, pitted
1   clove garlic
1   tsp. fresh lemon
½   tsp. sea salt
½   tsp. black pepper
¼   cup roasted red pepper, finely diced
3   tbsp. eggless mayonnaise

1. Blend eggplant with olives, garlic, lemon juice, salt and pepper in food processor until mixture is very smooth.

2. Stir in finely diced red peppers and mayonnaise to bind. Chill for 20 minutes to combine flavors. Serve open faced on toasted bread.

Makes 1½ cups

ALMOND SANDWICH FILLING

2   cups almonds, finely chopped
½   cup cream
¾   tsp. sea salt
¼   tsp. paprika
¼   tsp. pepper
2   tbsp. chives, finely chopped

1. Blend all ingredients together in blender or process in food processor until well mixed. Serve on pumpernickel bread.

Makes 2 cups

RED PEPPER AND CHILI SANDWICH

1	small red bell pepper
1	medium green chili
1	tsp. olive oil
1	clove garlic, minced
¼	tsp. vegesal
4	slices whole grain bread
2	slices tofu "Jack" cheese
2	oz. alfalfa sprouts

1. Roast pepper and chili in 450° oven until skin blisters. Place in a bowl, covered tightly with plastic wrap for 15 minutes. Remove skin, core and seeds. Cut into strips

2. Heat olive oil in a small skillet. Saute peppers and garlic until soft. Add vegesal. Continue to cook over medium heat for 3-5 minutes to combine flavors. Meanwhile toast bread.

3. Assemble sandwiches by placing peppers on toast followed by cheese, tomato and sprouts.

Serves 2

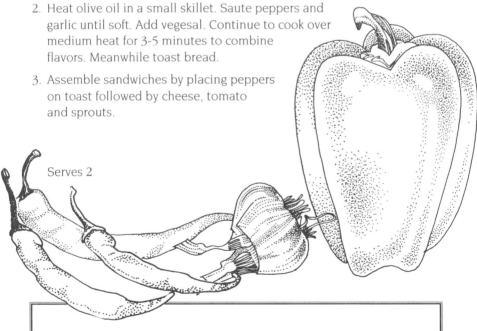

> **This is a great melted sandwich as well**.
> To assemble melted version:
> 1.Pre-heat broiler. Place peppers and cheese on 2 slices of toast. Broil 3-5 minutes to melt cheese. Top with tomatoes, sprouts and remaining toast.

BANANARAMMA

2 slices whole grain bread
1 tbsp. nut butter (cashew, almond, etc.)
1 tbsp. apple butter
½ medium banana, sliced lengthwise
1 oz. sprouts
½ tsp. cinnamon

1. Toast bread. Spread one slice with nut butter and the other with apple butter.
2. Place bananas, sprouts and cinnamon on one slice, top with the other.

Serves 1

TOFU SANDWICH SPREAD

32 oz. tofu
1   cup carrots, grated
½   cup green onions, sliced with tops
2   tbsp. nutritional yeast
2   tbsp. fresh lemon juice
1   tbsp. soy sauce
1   tbsp. olive oil
2   cloves garlic, crushed
2   tsp. curry powder
1   tsp. ginger powder

1. Drain tofu well. Meanwhile grate carrots and slice onions. Mash tofu with a fork until crumbly.
2. Mix all ingredients together until well blended. Let stand in the refrigerator for at least one hour.

This spread is great served on a seeded, whole grain bread with a variety of vegetables such as thinly sliced zucchini, cucumbers, tomatoes, and lettuce. You might also enjoy filling whole wheat pita pockets with tofu spread, sprouts and chopped vegetables.

Makes about 4 cups

CELERY, APPLE & WATERCRESS FILLING

1	cup watercress
½	cup celery, finely chopped
½	cup red apple, finely chopped with skin intact
⅓	cup eggless mayonnaise
¼	tsp. sea salt

1. Wash watercress. Discard any bruised leaves. Drain and chop finely.

2. Mix all ingredients well together. Serve on toasted whole wheat bread.

Makes 2 cups

TEJANO SANDWICH SPREAD

1	bunch green onions, sliced
2	cloves garlic
1	tbsp. cold pressed oil
1	medium green chili, finely chopped
1	tsp. salt
1	tsp. chili powder
½	tsp. cumin powder
2	cups black beans, cooked and well drained
¾	cup tofu "Jack" cheese, grated

1. Saute sliced onions and garlic in oil. Once onion has softened but not yet browned, add fresh chili, salt and spices. Continue to cook on low heat until chili has softened. Cool slightly.

2. Meanwhile mash beans with potato masher or fork. Do not use a food processor. Place in bowl. Add sauteed vegetables and cheese. Mix together well.

This spread can be used on a sandwich with additional roasted chilies and tomatoes, thinned slightly for a bean dip or served open faced on corn tortillas that have been oven fried.

Makes 3 cups.

APRICOT BUTTER SPREAD

1	cup drinking water
1	cup dried apricots, chopped finely
2	tbsp. honey
1	tsp. apple cider vinegar
6	tbsp. butter
1	tsp. cinnamon

1. Bring water to a boil in a non-corrosive pan. Add apricots, honey and vinegar. Cook over medium high heat until mixture thickens like syrup. Let stand to cool.

2. Place cooled apricot mixture in food processor using metal blade. Process for 1 minute or until smooth. Add butter and cinnamon, continue processing until well blended. Refrigerate.

This spread is excellent when paired in a sandwich with any nut butter. It is also an excellent accompaniment to freshly sliced fruit such as apples, pears or peaches

Makes 2 cups

HUMMUS

2   cups dried chick peas, soaked overnight and drained

<u>OR</u>

1   15 oz. can chick peas (garbanzo beans)
2   cloves garlic
3   tbsp. tahini
4   tbsp. fresh lemon juice
4   tbsp. olive oil
1   tbsp. fresh parsley, chopped
1   tsp. salt

1. If you are using dried chick peas, place them in sauce pan covered with water and add 1 tsp. sea salt. Bring to a boil and let simmer for 35-45 minutes until tender. Drain. After chick peas have cooled rub off as many skins as possible and proceed with recipe.
   If you are using canned chickpeas, rinse in colander and drain well.

2. Place chickpeas in food processor with garlic, tahini and lemon juice. Process until smooth. Slowly add olive oil to bind mixture. Add parsley and salt. Process until parsley is uniformly through garbanzo spread.

3. Chill for 20 minutes to combine flavors. Serve with pocket bread, sprouts and diced tomatoes.

Makes 2½ cups

NOTES

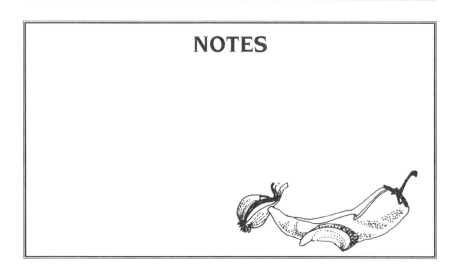

SCALLION ROUNDS

12   2 inch brown bread rounds
1   cup scallions, finely chopped
3   tbsp. eggless mayonnaise
1   tsp. tamari
¼   tsp. paprika

1. Toast bread round under broiler, turning after 2 minutes to insure uniform toasting on both sides.

2. Mix scallions, mayonnaise, tamari and paprika together well. Place about 1 tsp. of mixture on each bread round and place on a baking sheet. Place under broiler until the tops are golden brown.

Serves 4

BRUSCHETTA CON FUNGHI

½   lb. white mushrooms
4   tbsp. extra virgin olive oil
1   tbsp. fresh lemon juice
1   tbsp. fresh oregano leaves
1   tsp. sea salt
1   tsp. freshly ground pepper
4-6 slices country bread, thickly sliced
2   cloves garlic, peeled and cut in half
1½ tbsp. extra virgin olive oil.

1. Wipe mushrooms with a damp cloth. Trim stems, then thinly slice and place in ceramic bowl. Add olive oil, lemon, oregano, salt and pepper. Toss gently for 2 minutes until mushrooms slightly soften.

2. Grill or toast bread. Rub with cut side of garlic and lightly drizzle with oil.

3. Spoon mushroom mixture over bread, drizzle with remaining oil and serve.

Serves 4-6

BRUSCHETTA WITH OLIVE PASTE

2   cups oil cured black olives, pitted
1½   tbsp. extra virgin olive oil
2   medium tomatoes, finely diced
8   large basil leaves, coarsely chopped
1   tsp. sea salt
6   slices country bread, thickly sliced
2   cloves garlic, peeled and cut in half

1. Place olives in food processor. Process to form smooth paste, adding olive oil in small amounts as necessary to form paste.

2. Mix tomatoes and basil together in small bowl. Season with sea salt. Set aside to allow flavors to blend.

3. Grill or toast bread. Rub with cut side of garlic and lightly drizzle with additional oil. Spread each slice with olive paste, topped with a tbsp. of tomato mixture.

Serves 6

BRUSCHETTA WITH TOMATOES

2   **large ripe tomatoes**
4   **slices country bread, thickly sliced**
2   **garlic cloves, peeled and cut in half**
4   **tbsp. extra virgin olive oil**
1   **tsp. sea salt**
4   **large basil leaves**

1. Very lightly roast tomatoes over an outdoor grill or gas burner. Peel, then cut horizontally to remove all seeds. Cut tomato halves into strips.

2. Grill or toast bread. Rub with cut side of garlic and lightly drizzle with olive oil.

3. Place tomato strips on toast, salt lightly with sea salt. Tear basil leaves into pieces and place over tomatoes. Drizzle with remaining olive oil. Serve warm.

Serves 2

NOTES

ARTICHOKE AND BLACK OLIVE SANDWICH

1   cup oil cured black olives, pitted
3   tbsp. extra virgin olive oil
10   baby artichokes or 1 15 OZ. canned artichokes
1   lemon, cut in half
1   tsp. sea salt
1   tsp. black pepper
1   clove garlic, peeled and crushed
4   whole wheat, sour dough rolls

1. Puree olives in food processor. Add a bit of oil if needed to make smooth paste. Set aside.

2. Trim artichokes of tough leaves, using ½ of the lemon to rub cut portions to keep them from turning brown. Place in large pot, cover with water and salt. Boil rapidly until hearts are tender. Drain well. If using canned chokes, rinse and drain well.

3. Trim chokes from center, cut in quarters and place in a bowl. Add juice from remaining lemon half, olive oil, pepper and crushed garlic. Mix well and set side for at least one hour.

4. Cut rolls in half horizontally, spread bottom half of each roll with olive paste. Top with artichoke quarters. Season lightly with additional salt and pepper. Top with other half of bread.

Serves 4

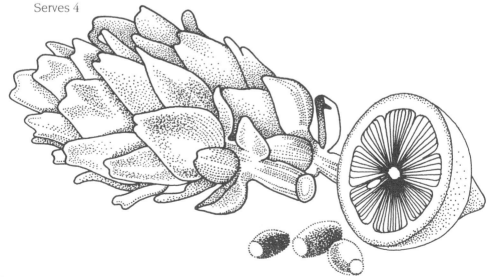

GRILLED TOFU "JACK"

4   **tbsp. butter**
4   **slices whole grain bread**
8   **slices tofu "Jack" cheese**
4   **slices ripe tomato**
4   **slices ripe avocado**
2   **scallions, thinly sliced**

1. Melt 2 tbsp. of butter in a large skillet. Place 2 slices of bread into skillet. Top with cheese slices, tomatoes, avocados and scallions, then remaining slices of bread.

2. Cook over medium head until bread is well browned. Add remaining butter to skillet and turn sandwiches. Serve when other side has browned.

Serves 2

ITALIAN HERO

1   **long loaf whole wheat sourdough bread**
4   **tbsp. eggless mayonnaise (optional)**
1   **large tomato, thinly sliced**
2   **tbsp. olive oil**
1   **tbsp. fresh basil, chopped**
1   **medium zucchini, thinly sliced**
½   **tsp. sea salt**
½   **tsp. freshly ground black pepper**
½   **lb. tofu "jack" cheese, thinly sliced**
1   **medium red onion, very thinly sliced**
1   **medium green pepper, sliced into paper thin rounds**
2   **tbsp. pepperoncini, chopped**

1. Slice loaf in half lengthwise. Spread with mayonnaise, if desired.

2. Divide fillings into halves. Layer with half of the tomatoes, then sprinkle lightly with oil and basil. Next, layer with zucchini, then sprinkle with salt and pepper. Then layer cheese, followed by onion and green pepper. Sprinkle with pepperoncini.

3. Repeat layers and place top of bread over layered filling.

Serves 4

PIZZA VERDI

DOUGH

2	tsp. active dry yeast
1	cup warm water
1½	cup whole wheat flour
½	cup whole wheat pastry flour
1	tsp. sea salt
2	tbsp. olive oil

FILLING

1½	cups tofu cheese, grated
1	cup green onions, sliced thinly
1	cup green bell peppers, chopped
½	cup green olives, sliced
¼	cup fresh basil leaves, sliced thinly
¼	cup extra virgin olive oil
1	tsp. sea salt
1	tsp. freshly ground pepper

1. Dissolve yeast in warm water. Mix dry ingredients together. Add yeast mixture and oil to form soft dough. Knead for 10 minutes on floured surface to make a silky dough, adding more flour or water as necessary. Set to rise in warm place for 1 hour. Punch dough down and allow to rise again for ½ hour.

2. While dough is rising second time, preheat oven to 450°. Roll dough out on 14" oiled pizza pan. Fold over edges to hold filling.

3. Place tofu cheese on pizza followed by onions, peppers, olives and basil leaves. Drizzle with a little more oil. Sprinkle with salt and pepper.

4. Bake for 20 minutes on lowest rack of oven until crust is browned.

Serves 4

NOTES

POTATO AND ARUGULA PIZZA

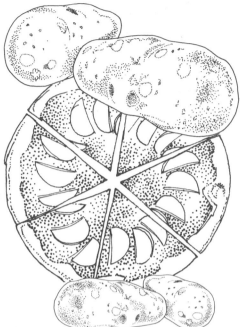

DOUGH

2	tsp. active dry yeast
1	cup warm water
1½	cup whole wheat flour
½	cup whole wheat pastry flour
1	tsp. sea salt
2	tbsp. olive oil

FILLING

1	lb. baking potatoes
4	tbsp. extra virgin olive oil
1	tsp. coarse sea salt
2	cloves garlic, peeled and mashed
¼	tsp. red pepper flakes
2	tbsp. freshly grated parmesan cheese
½	cup arugula leaves, stemmed and cut

1. Dissolve yeast in warm water. Mix dry ingredients together. Add yeast mixture and oil to form soft dough. Knead for 10 minutes on floured surface to make a silky dough, adding more flour or water as necessary. Set to rise in a warm place for 1 hour. Punch dough down and allow to rise again for ½ hour.

2. Peel potatoes, slice thinly. Toss gently with 2 tbsp. of olive oil. Arrange potato slices on a baking sheet in a single layer. Bake at 350° until potatoes begin to brown. Remove from oven. Sprinkle with salt.

3. Combine remaining olive oil with mashed garlic.

4. While dough is rising second time, preheat oven to 450°. Roll dough out on 14" oiled pizza pan. Fold over edges to hold filling. Brush with olive oil mixture and sprinkle with red pepper flakes. Arrange potatoes over top in an overlapping pattern. Brush with remaining olive oil mixture. Top with grated cheese. Place on lowest rack of oven for 20 minutes until crust is well browned.

5. Remove from oven and sprinkle with arugula just before serving.

Serves 4

SPINACH CALZONE

DOUGH

2	tsp. active dry yeast
1	cup warm water
1½	cup whole wheat flour
½	cup whole wheat pastry flour
1	tsp. sea salt
2	tbsp. olive oil

FILLING

4	tbsp. olive oil
½	cup red onions, thinly sliced
½	cup red peppers, diced
1	cup black olives
2	cloves garlic, peeled and mashed
3	cups fresh spinach, stemmed and torn
1	tsp. sea salt
1	tsp. black pepper
2	cups tofu cheese, grated

1. Dissolve yeast in warm water. Mix dry ingredients together. Add yeast mixture and oil to form soft dough. Knead for 10 minutes on lightly floured surface to make a silky dough, adding more flour or water as necessary. Set to rise in a warm place for 1 hour. Punch dough down and allow to rise again for ½ hour.

2. Meanwhile, heat 2 tbsp. of olive oil in large skillet. Add onions and red peppers. Cook over medium heat until onions are translucent. Add olives and garlic. Cook 3 minutes more. Add spinach, salt and pepper. Turn heat to high for 1 minute and cover to barely wilt spinach. Cool mixture. Gently toss with cheese.

3. While dough is rising second time, preheat oven to 450°. Roll dough into 12-14 inch circle. Place on baking sheet or pizza stone. Place spinach mixture on one half of dough. Fold other half over first, then crimp edges making sure to seal completely. Brush top with remaining oil.

4. Bake on lowest rack of oven for 20 minutes or until crust is richly browned. Cool for 5 minutes, then serve.

Serves 2

FALAFELS

FALAFEL MIX

4	cups garbanzo beans, cooked rinsed and drained
OR	
2	15 oz. cans garbanzo beans, rinsed and drained
¼	cup celery, chopped
3	cloves garlic, peeled
½	cup onion, chopped
¼	cup bread crumbs
2	tbsp. tahini
½	tsp. cumin
¼	tsp. turmeric
¼	tsp. cayenne
1	tsp. sea salt
1	tsp. black pepper
2	tbsp. olive oil

SANDWICH

1	tbsp. lemon juice
6	oz. heavy cream
6	whole wheat pita rounds
1	small cucumber, thinly sliced
12	cherry tomatoes
3	scallions
4	ounces alfalfa sprouts
1	tbsp. dill
2	cloves garlic, peeled and mashed

1. Process all falafel mix ingredients in food processor until smooth. Form mixture into 1" balls (makes about 48). Placed on lightly oiled baking sheet and bake in 350° oven for 15 minutes or until golden brown.

2. Meanwhile, stir lemon juice into cream. Let sit at room temperature to sour.

3. Divide and split pita rounds. Cover and warm in oven for 5 minutes.

4. Remove pitas from oven. Divide cucumbers, tomatoes, scallions and sprouts among pita halves. Tuck 4 falafel in each sandwich. Place on serving platter.

5. Stir dill and garlic into soured cream. Serve as dressing for falafel sandwiches.

Serves 6

CARROTY WICH

2   cups carrots, scrubbed and shredded

¼   cup golden raisins, chopped

¼   cup cashews, chopped

¼   tsp. cinnamon

2   tbsp. lime juice

½   cup eggless mayonnaise

4   slices whole grain bread

1. Toss carrots, raisins, cashews, cinnamon and lime juice together. Bind with mayonnaise.

2. Divide carrot mixture onto two slices of bread. Top with remaining 2 slices.

Serves 2

TERIYAKI SANDWICH

12   oz. firm tofu, cut in thin slices

4   oz. teriyaki sauce

1   small whole wheat sourdough loaf

2   cups tofu "jackmelt" cheese, grated

2   tbsp. green onions, thinly sliced

3   tbsp. eggless mayonnaise

2   tsp. hot oriental mustard

1. Place tofu slices in shallow bowl. Marinate in teriyaki sauce.

2. Slice bread lengthwise. Mix cheese with green onions. Place on bottom half of bread and toast briefly under broiler to slightly melt cheese.

3. Add tofu slices on top of melted cheese, drizzle with remaining marinade. Return to broiler 3-5 minutes to brown.

4. Meanwhile, mix mayonnaise with hot mustard. Spread on top half of loaf. When bottom half is removed from oven, top and serve.

Serves 4

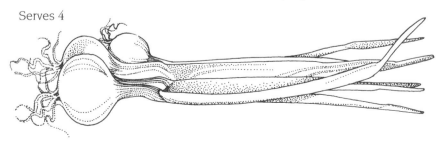

SUNSET MELT

2	tbsp. eggless mayonnaise
2	tsp. dijon mustard
2	whole wheat English muffins, split
1	medium avocado, sliced
½	cup radishes, scrubbed and thinly sliced
1	small carrot, scrubbed and shredded
4	mushrooms, thinly sliced
1	cup tofu "jack" cheese, shredded
2	oz. alfalfa sprouts

1. Mix mayonnaise and mustard together. Spread on muffin halves.

2. Layer all vegetables except sprouts on muffins. Top with cheese. Place under broiler for 5-7 minutes until cheese is bubbly. Top with sprouts.

Serves 2

HOT PITA SPLITS

1	tbsp. olive oil
1	tsp. thyme
¼	tsp. sea salt
¼	tsp. black pepper
2	large whole wheat pita rounds
1	cup tofu cheese, shredded
½	cup tomatoes, diced
¼	cup black olives
¼	cup red onion, thinly sliced
¼	cup sunflower seeds

1. Mix together olive oil, thyme, salt and pepper.

2. Split pita rounds horizontally. Layer with tofu cheese followed by tomatoes, olives, and onions. Drizzle with seasoned olive oil. Sprinkle with sunflower seeds.

3. Broil 3-5 minutes until tofu cheese is brown and bubbly.

Serves 2

QUICK PITA SPLITS

¼   cup eggless mayonnaise

1   tbsp. dijon mustard

2   tsp. honey

2   large whole wheat pita rounds

½   cup scallions, sliced thinly

½   cup carrot, shredded

½   large cucumber, sliced thinly

8   mushrooms, sliced thinly

¼   cup sliced black olives

¼   cup almonds, chopped

1. Mix mayonnaise, mustard and honey together in small bowl.

2. Split pitas horizontally. Spread with seasoned mayonnaise. Top with vegetables and nuts.

Serves 2

MUSHROOM MELT

2   tbsp. butter

2   cups mushrooms, sliced

½   tsp. ginger, ground

1   clove garlic

2   tsp. tamari

1   tsp. dulse seaweed, finely chopped

1   tsp. honey

2   whole wheat English muffins, split

¼   cup scallions, sliced thinly

½   cup tofu cheese, shredded

1. Heat butter in saute pan. Add mushrooms, ginger and garlic. Cook over medium heat until mushrooms begin to soften. Add tamari, dulse and honey. Reduce heat to low and cook for 3 minutes.

2. Toast muffins. Pile mushroom mixture on toasted halves. Top with scallions and cheese. Place under broiler 3-5 minutes to melt cheese until brown and bubbly.

Serves 2

APPLE CHEESE MELT

2	tbsp. butter
½	cup yellow onion, thinly sliced
1	tsp. fresh thyme
2	whole wheat English muffins
1	large red apple, washed and sliced thinly
1	cup tofu "jack" cheese, shredded

1. Heat butter in saute pan. When bubbly, add onions. Cook for 15 minutes over low heat until onions are translucent and very soft. Add thyme.

2. Toast muffin splits. Spread onion mixture evenly over toasted rounds. Layer with apple slices. Top with cheese. Place under broiler 3-5 minutes until cheese is brown and bubbly.

Serves 2

VEGGIE QUESADILLA

2   tbsp. butter

1   cup tofu "jack"cheese, shredded

1   small zucchini, sliced thinly

4   mushrooms, sliced thinly

1   cup spinach, torn into small pieces

2   tbsp. sweet onions, finely diced

2   tsp. ortega chilies, diced

2   whole wheat flour tortillas

1. Heat butter in large skillet.
2. Place cheese and all vegetables on one half of each tortilla. Fold over. Place in skillet with cheese side closest to fire. Cook over medium heat until tortilla is nicely brown. Flip to brown other side and wilt vegetables.
3. Serve with guacamole and salsa.

Serves 2

NOTES

SALADS & DRESSINGS

SALADS AND DRESSINGS

GRAINS, ROOTS, LEAVES AND DELICIOUS COMPLEMENTS

In almost every study of longevity, of cultures with low disease rates, of people in virtually every society (including ours) who never get sick, you'll find a common thread among the factors contributing to the health of the target group --raw vegetables! This is because the state in which any vegetable is at its most nutritious, immune-boosting level, is in its most natural state: raw and fresh out of your garden or from an organically cultivated produce market.

For this reason, the salads in this section are always prepared with the freshest, raw vegetables you can find. There are absolutely no limitations to how you might combine fresh, seasonal vegetables to create salads that provide either a main course or side dish for any meal. We have also included many recipes that will give you an idea of how to combine vegetables to complement one another.

Don't get caught up in the "baby vegetable" fad that many "foodies" advocate. For salads to be high in abscisic acid, the immune-boosting nutrient we mentioned in our introduction -- vegetables must be past the youthful rapid growth spurt and at the mature stage in which they are producing the plant hormones called abscisins. Immature vegetables contain high amounts of gibberellins, the very hormones that neutralize the abscisins.

Dressing recipes are called for in many of the salad recipes, but others are presented for you to create your own. As with every recipe the the book, we suggest that you purchase the finest ingredients for use in dressings, as they provide not only zest to the recipe, but oftentimes have a catalytic effect on the ingredients, making them interact to create a whole new flavor sensation.

Although many dressing recipes call for the use of oils, remember that the amount noted is for *all* the servings in the recipe. Therefore, each serving will always provide less than one tablespoon of oil. Since you are no longer including animal fats in your diet, these oils are important for the assimilation of the fat-soluble vitamins, especially A and E.

We hope you find these recipes an exciting addition to your culinary repertoire as you explore a more healthful manner of eating.

CLEMENTE'S POTATO SALAD

2	lbs. white potatoes, scrubbed
3	tbsp. cider vinegar
1	large red bell pepper, seeded and diced
1	bunch green onions with tops, sliced
2	stalks celery, sliced finely
1½	cups eggless mayonnaise or San Pasqual mayonnaise
1	tsp. sea salt
1	tsp. black pepper
1	tsp. celery seed
⅛	tsp. paprika

1. Boil potatoes in water until tender when pierced but still firm. Drain, then dice into ½ inch cubes. Sprinkle with vinegar.

2. Add red bell pepper, green onions and celery. Fold in mayonnaise, sea salt, pepper, celery seed and paprika.

Serves 6

BLACK BEAN SALAD

4	cups black beans, cooked
2	ribs celery, thinly sliced
2	avocados, peeled and cut into cubes
1	large red or green bell pepper, seeded and diced
1	medium red onion, thinly sliced
2	cups Papaya Mango Salsa (see page 118)
½	cup olive oil

1. Toss all ingredients together in large bowl. Let stand for 30 minutes to blend flavors.

Serves 4-6

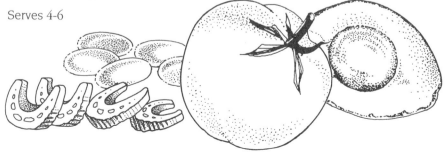

FRENCH POTATO SALAD

1	lb. new red potatoes, unpeeled
6	scallions with tops, sliced thinly
1	large red bell pepper, seeded and diced
1	6 oz. can marinated artichokes, drained
1	cup Lemon Dressing (see page 113)
1	clove garlic, peeled and mashed
1	tbsp. Dijon style mustard
2	tbsp. soy "Parmesan" cheese

1. Boil potatoes in water until tender when pierced but still firm. Drain, then cut into quarters or sixths depending on size of potatoes. Add scallions, bell pepper and artichokes.

2. In a small mixing bowl, whisk Lemon Dressing, garlic and mustard until well blended. Toss with potato mixture. Gently fold in cheese. May be served warm or chilled.

Serves 4

EASY THREE BEAN SALAD

2	cups kidney beans, cooked
2	cups garbanzos, cooked
2	cups black-eyed peas, cooked
½	cup fresh peas or frozen petite peas, thawed
¼	cup parsley, chopped
6	green onions with tops, finely sliced
2	cloves garlic, crushed
1	cup Lemon Dressing (see page 113)

1. Drain beans from their liquids. Rinse lightly.

2. Combine beans with peas, parsley, onions and garlic. Toss gently with dressing. Let stand for at least 2 hours for flavors to blend.

Serves 4

CHINESE GREEN NOODLE SALAD

1½   cups Cashew Nut Dressing (see page 115)
½   tsp. ginger, ground or 1 tsp. fresh grated
1   tbsp. toasted sesame oil
1   tsp. hot spicy Chinese mustard (optional)
1   lb. Chinese thin rice noodles,cooked and drained
½   lb. broccoli, lightly steamed and cut into
   bite-sized florets
½   lb. asparagus, lightly steamed and cut into
   bite-sized pieces
1   cup Shitake or other Oriental mushrooms, sliced
4   scallions with tops, sliced

1. In a small bowl, whisk together Cashew Nut Dressing with ginger, sesame oil and mustard.

2. In large bowl, toss together Chinese noodles, broccoli, asparagus, mushrooms and scallions. Add dressing, tossing well to coat noodles. Chill for 15 minutes to allow flavors to blend.

Serves 4

JERUSALEM ARTICHOKE SALAD

6   Jerusalem artichokes, washed and grated
3   ribs celery, sliced thinly
2   large carrots, scrubbed and grated
1   large green apple, cored and diced
1   cup green cabbage, finely shredded
2   tbsp. parsley, finely chopped
2   tbsp. pumpkin seeds
1   cup Creamy Cucumber Dressing (see page 115)

1. Place all ingredients in large serving bowl. Toss with dressing and serve.

Serves 4

MOROCCAN COUS COUS SALAD

1¼	cups drinking water
1½	cups dry cous cous
2	carrots, scrubbed and sliced on diagonal
½	lb. green beans, trimmed and sliced on diagonal
1	green bell pepper, seeded and diced
½	small sweet red onion, diced
⅓	cup golden raisins
½	cup almonds, sliced and lightly toasted
1	cup Cinnamon Mint Dressing (see page 113)

1. Bring water to boil. Add cous cous. Cover and remove from heat. Allow to sit 15 minutes until all liquid is absorbed, then fluff with a fork.

2. Meanwhile, lightly steam carrot and green beans until just tender crisp.

3. Toss all ingredients together. Allow to stand for 15 minutes to allow flavors to blend.

Serves 4

CASHEW PEA SALAD

½	cup Tofu Dressing (see page 113)
1	tsp. chives, snipped
1	tsp. parsley, freshly chopped
1	lb. snow peas, trimmed and stringed
1½	cups fresh peas or frozen petite peas
4	scallions with tops, sliced
¼	lb. mushrooms, brushed clean with a vegetable brush and sliced
½	cup cashews, coarsely chopped

1. In a small bowl, mix together Tofu Dressing with chives and parsley. Set aside.

2. In a salad bowl, place snow peas, peas, scallions and mushrooms. Toss gently with dressing. Top with cashews.

Serves 4

QUINOA & BEET SALAD

2	cups drinking water
2	tsp. sea salt
1	cup quinoa
3	tbsp. orange juice
½	cup olive oil or walnut oil
½	tsp. black pepper
¼	cup currants
3	beets, boiled and cubed
4	scallions with tops, sliced
1	rib celery, thinly sliced
2	tbsp. chives, chopped
1	tbsp. fresh mint, chopped
1	lb. spinach leaves, washed and torn

1. Bring water and 1 tsp. salt to boil. Add quinoa. Cover and simmer for 10 minutes until slightly chewy. Drain.

2. In small mixing bowl, whisk together orange juice, oil, 1 tsp. salt and pepper. Set aside.

3. In large bowl, toss quinoa with currants, beets, scallions, celery, chives and mint. Toss with dressing. Allow to sit for 20 minutes for flavors to blend. Place spinach leaves on individual plates or on serving platter. Mound quinoa mixture in center and serve.

Serves 4-6

NOTES

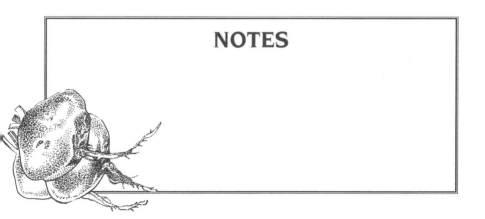

Quick Artichoke Pasta Salad

4	quarts water
2	tbsp. sea salt
1	lb. whole wheat salad macaroni or other medium sized pasta
1	6 oz. jar marinated artichoke hearts, sliced into quarters, marinade reserved
¼	lb. mushrooms brushed clean with a vegetable brush, quartered
1	cup cherry tomatoes, halved
1	tbsp. parsley, chopped
1	tbsp. fresh basil leaves, chopped finely
2	tsp. black pepper, ground coarsely

1. Bring 4 quarts of water with sea salt to boil in a large pot and cook macaroni according to package directions. Do not over cook. It should be firm to the bite. Drain pasta and place in a large stainless steel or glass bowl.

2. Add remaining ingredients including reserved marinade from artichokes. Refrigerate for at least two hours, however, overnight is preferable so that flavors have a chance to blend. Adjust seasoning.

Serves 6

Green Garden Salad

1	head romaine lettuce, washed and leaves torn
1	cup garbanzo beans, cooked
8	cherry tomatoes, quartered
1	small zucchini, grated
1	small carrot, grated
4	radishes, scrubbed and sliced thinly
¼	cup raw sunflower seeds
¼	cup raw pumpkin seeds
½	cup Green Goddess Dressing (see page 116)

1. Toss vegetables and seeds together. Serve with Green Goddess dressing.

Serves 4

WALDORF SALAD

½   cup eggless mayonnaise or San Pasqual mayonnaise
2   tbsp. lemon juice
1   tsp. hot sweet mustard
2   large red apples, cored and diced
1   cup celery, diced
1   cup seedless grapes, halved
½   cup walnuts, lightly toasted
1   head soft green lettuce, washed and torn

1. In small bowl, whisk together mayonnaise, lemon juice and mustard.

2. Place apples, celery, grapes and walnuts together in a bowl. Toss with dressing. Arrange lettuce leaves on a platter or individual plates. Mound salad on top of lettuce and serve.

Serves 4

NOTES

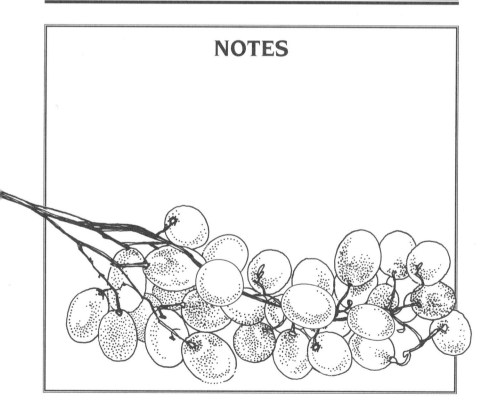

TABBOULEH

1 cup bulgar wheat
½ cup fresh lemon juice
4 medium ripe tomatoes, seeded and chopped
2 medium cucumbers, seeded and chopped
4 green onions with tops, finely sliced
½ cup fresh parsley, finely chopped
1 tbsp. fresh mint or ½ tsp. dried
¼ cup olive oil
1 tsp. sea salt
2 cups Adzuki beans, cooked

1. Place wheat in a stainless steel or glass bowl. Pour lemon juice over wheat. Add just enough warm water to barely cover. Let stand for ½ hour to absorb the moisture.

2. Meanwhile, prepare all other ingredients. Add all ingredients. Refrigerate for at least 2 hours to blend flavors.

Serves 4-6

NOTES

RISING SUN ORIENTAL SALAD

½	cup Adzuki beans, cooked
½	cup black beans, cooked
½	cup black eyed peas, cooked
½	cup brown rice, cooked
½	cup wild rice, cooked
½	medium red onion, thinly sliced
⅓	cup fresh lemon juice
1	tbsp. tamari
1	clove fresh garlic, finely chopped
1	tsp. curry powder
1	medium knob fresh ginger, grated or 1 tsp. ground
2	tsp. black pepper
⅔	cup olive oil
1	medium carrot, julienned
¼	lb. Shitake mushrooms, sliced
¼	lb. snow peas, trimmed and sliced on the diagonal in thirds
1	cup Adzuki, garbanzo & lentil sprouts combined OR
1	cup bean sprouts

1. Place beans and rice into large stainless steel or glass bowl.

2. In small mixing bowl, place lemon juice, tamari, garlic, curry powder, ginger and pepper. Gradually add olive oil and continue to beat until well emulsified.

3. Pour dressing over bean/rice mixture. Add remaining vegetables. Toss well then chill for 2 hours before serving.

Serves 6

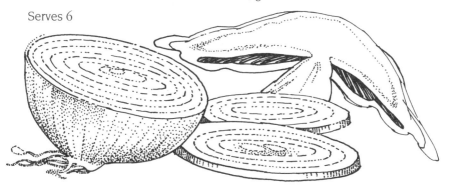

TACO SALAD

1	head green leaf lettuce, washed and torn
4	medium tomatoes, cored and quartered
1	large avocado, peeled and diced
1	ear fresh corn, cut from cob
½	small red onion, diced
1	15 oz. can red kidney or black beans, drained
1	cup soy "Jack" cheese, grated
4	oz. corn chips make from organically grown corn
½	cup eggless mayonnaise (optional)
1	cup Salsa Mexicano (see page 120)

1. Place lettuce in large serving bowl. Add other vegetables, topped with cheese and corn chips.

2. If using mayonnaise, mix well with salsa. Pour over salad. If not using mayonnaise, just top with salsa and serve.

Serves 4

PINEAPPLE SLAW

½	cup Lime Poppy Seed Dressing (see page 112)
¼	cup eggless mayonnaise
1	small head green cabbage, sliced thinly
½	cup fresh pineapple, peeled, cored and diced
1	green apple, cored and diced
4	scallions with tops, sliced thinly

1. In small bowl, mix Lime Poppy Seed Dressing with mayonnaise.

2. Place all other ingredients in a large bowl. Toss with dressing. Chill for 20 minutes to allow flavors to blend.

Serves 4-6

SUNFLOWER SALAD

2   cups sunflower sprouts
2   cups carrots, scrubbed and grated
1   cup celery, chopped finely
1   cup Tomato Herb Dressing (see page 114)

1. Toss sprouts, carrots and celery together. Just before serving, gently toss with dressing.

Serves 4

7 LAYER FRUIT SALAD

1   pint strawberries, hulled and sliced
4   large peaches, peeled and sliced
1   pint blueberries, washed
2   large bananas, peeled and sliced
2   large oranges, peeled, sectioned and cut into bite-sized pieces

5   tsp. fresh lime juice
6   tbsp. coconut, unsweetened

1   cup whipped cream (see page 237)
½   cup granola or toasted nuts

1. Assemble layers in 3 quart, clear glass salad bowl. Begin with strawberries. Sprinkle with 1 tsp. lime juice followed by 1 tbsp. coconut. Continue layering fruit in order given, sprinkling each layer with 1 tsp. lime juice and 1 tbsp. coconut as you go. When all fruit has been layered in dish, top with whipped cream. Chill for 15 minutes.

2. Top with granola or nuts just prior to serving.

Serves 4-6

PECAN SPINACH SALAD

1	cup eggless mayonnaise or San Pasqual mayonnaise
2	tbsp. pineapple juice
2	lb. fresh spinach, washed and torn
2	ribs celery, sliced thinly
1	cup fresh pineapple, peeled and diced
2	tbsp. red onion, finely chopped
1	bunch radishes, washed and sliced thinly
1	cup pecan halves, lightly toasted
1	tbsp. soy "bacon" bits (optional)

1. In small mixing bowl, mix mayonnaise with pineapple juice. Set aside.

2. In large salad bowl, place torn spinach. Add celery, pineapple, red onions and radishes. Top with pecans and soy bits. (optional) Serve with mayonnaise dressing.

Serves 4

CABBAGE GLOW SALAD

1	cup carrots, scrubbed and grated
1	cup beets, peeled and grated
1	stalk celery, sliced thinly
1	cup red cabbage, finely shredded
2	cups green leaf lettuce, torn
2	tbsp. sunflower seeds
½	cup Blueberry Vinaigrette (see page 112)

1. In a bowl, toss carrots, beets and celery together.

2. Divide lettuce leaves among four plates. Mound ¼ cup cabbage in center of each. Place carrot mixture around cabbage to form a ring. Sprinkle with sunflower seeds, then drizzle with blueberry vinaigrette.

Serves 4

RAW ROOT SALAD

1	tbsp. horseradish, grated if fresh or drained
½	cup eggless mayonnaise or San Pasqual mayonnaise
½	cup parsnips, scrubbed and grated
½	cup turnips, scrubbed and grated
½	cup sweet potato, peeled and grated
½	cup potato, scrubbed and grated
2	scallions with tops, sliced thinly
½	red bell pepper, seeded and diced
4	large romaine lettuce leaves

1. Mix horseradish with mayonnaise. Add grated vegetables, scallions and peppers tossing gently to mix well.

2. Place a lettuce leaf on each serving plate, mound grated root mixture into center of each and serve.

Serves 4

NORTH AFRICAN SALAD

¼	cup olive oil
¼	cup lime juice
½	tsp. sea salt
½	tsp. black pepper
1	large seedless cucumber, halved and sliced thinly
2	large tomatoes, cut into six wedges each
4	scallions with tops, sliced
2	tbsp. fresh mint, chopped

1. In a small bowl, whisk together olive oil, lime juice, salt and pepper. Set aside.

2. Toss cucumber, tomato wedges, scallions and mint together. Toss gently with dressing. Chill for at least 20 minutes to blend flavors.

Serves 4

CARROT, APPLE & RAISIN SALAD

2	tbsp. lime juice
3	tbsp. safflower oil
1	tsp. spike seasoning
1	tbsp. tamari
2	large red apples, cored and diced (2 cups)
4	carrots, grated
½	cup golden raisins
1	small head butter lettuce, washed and separated into individual leaves

1. In a small mixing bowl, combine lime juice, tamari and spike. Slowly add oil and whisk until emulsified.

2. Toss apples, carrots and raisins together in a bowl. Gently toss with dressing. Line platter with lettuce leaves. Mound salad in middle and serve.

Serves 4

TOMATO, RED ONION & TOFU SALAD

¼	cup balsamic vinegar
½	cup olive oil
½	tsp. sea salt
½	tsp. black pepper, freshly ground
8	oz. firm tofu, drained for ½ hour, then cut into ¼" slabs
4	large ripe tomato, cored and sliced
1	medium sweet red onion, sliced
2	tbsp. fresh basil, chopped

1. In a medium glass bowl, mix together, vinegar, oil, salt and pepper. Add tofu slices. Allow to marinate for 20 minutes. Drain and reserve marinade.

2. On a serving platter, alternately arrange tomato slices, onion slices and tofu slices. Drizzle with reserved marinade. Garnish with fresh basil.

Serves 4

AVOCADO FIESTA SALAD

⅓ cup fresh lemon juice
1 clove fresh garlic, mashed
1 tsp. oregano
½ tsp. red pepper
½ tsp. paprika
½ tsp. sea salt
2 tbsp. fresh cilantro, finely chopped (optional)
⅔ cup cold pressed corn oil
½ cup Adzuki beans, cooked
2 large avocados, peeled and cubed
1 large ripe tomato, seeded and chopped
½ medium red onion, medium diced
2 green onions, sliced with tops
½ cup fresh corn, cut from cob
2 tbsp. fresh parsley, finely chopped
1 head romaine lettuce or mixed greens

1. In a small bowl, mix lemon juice with garlic, oregano, red pepper, paprika, sea salt and cilantro. Gradually add oil. Continue to beat until well emulsified.

2. Pour dressing over Adzuki beans. Let stand for 30 minutes to absorb flavors.

3. Gently toss with avocados, tomatoes, red onion, green onion, corn and parsley. Serve on bed of lettuce.

Serves 4

NOTES

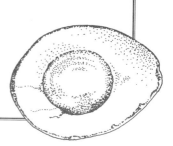

BLUEBERRY VINAIGRETTE

½ cup blueberries, fresh or frozen-thawed
⅓ cup drinking water
1 tbsp. rice or apple cider vinegar <u>OR</u>
2 tbsp. lemon juice
2 tbsp. olive oil or walnut oil
1 clove fresh garlic, chopped
½ tsp. oregano
½ tsp. mustard seeds
⅛ tsp. ginger, ground

1. Blend all ingredients together in a blender.

Makes 1 cup

LIME POPPY SEED DRESSING

3 tbsp. lime juice
2 tbsp. raw honey
¼ tsp. sea salt
⅛ tsp. ground mace
½ cup safflower oil
½ tsp. lime peel, grated
1½ tsp. poppy seeds

1. Place lime juice, honey, sea salt and mace in blender. Blend well. Slowly, add oil in a thin, steady stream, continue blending until all oil is emulsified. Stir in lime peel and poppy seeds

Makes 1 cup

LEMON DRESSING

⅓   cup lemon juice
1   clove garlic
½   tsp. sea salt
½   tsp. black pepper
⅔   cup olive oil

1. Combine lemon juice, garlic, salt and pepper. Slowly drizzle in oil and continue to beat until well emulsified.

Makes 1 cup

CINNAMON MINT DRESSING

½   cup olive oil
⅓   cup lemon juice
3   tbsp. orange juice
½   tsp. lemon pepper
½   tsp. cinnamon
⅛   tsp. paprika
½   tsp. fresh orange peel, grated
1   tbsp. fresh mint, finely chopped

1. Place all ingredients except orange peel and mint in blender. Blend until smooth. Stir in orange peel and mint.

Makes 1⅓ cups

TOFU DRESSING

16   oz. soft tofu, well drained
½   cup tamari soy sauce
1   clove garlic
3   cups drinking water
1   cup sesame seeds

1. Place tofu, soy sauce, garlic and water in blender. Blend until smooth. Stir in sesame seeds.

Makes 1 quart

TOMATO HERB DRESSING

1   large tomato, quartered
1   15 oz. canned tomatoes, chopped in juice
1   small onion, chopped
1   clove garlic, peeled
2   tbsp. olive oil
1   tbsp. cider vinegar
1   tbsp. lemon juice
1   tsp. dried tarragon, whole
1   tsp. dried basil, whole
1   tsp. paprika
1   tsp. sea salt
1   tsp. Spike

1. Place all ingredients in blender. Blend until smooth.

Makes 3½ cups

TAHINI DRESSING

1   cup Tahini
1   cup cucumber, finely diced
1   cup ripe tomato, finely diced
1   tbsp. mint, finely chopped
1   tsp. cilantro, finely chopped
2-3   tbsp. water

1. Mix tahini with cucumber, tomato, mint and cilantro. Add water to reach consistency of light cream.

Makes 3 cups

CASHEW NUT DRESSING

1¼   cups raw cashews
1¼   cups drinking water
½   cup safflower or olive oil
¼   cup lemon juice
2   cloves garlic, peeled
2   tsp. onion powder
1   tbsp. vegesal

1. Place all ingredients in a blender. Blend until smooth and creamy.

Makes 3 cups

CREAMY CUCUMBER DRESSING

1   large cucumber, peeled
½   green bell pepper, chopped
½   small onion, chopped
1   cup soy milk
1   tsp. apple juice
1   tsp. dried basil
1   tbsp. tamari

1. Place all ingredients in blender.
   Blend until smooth.

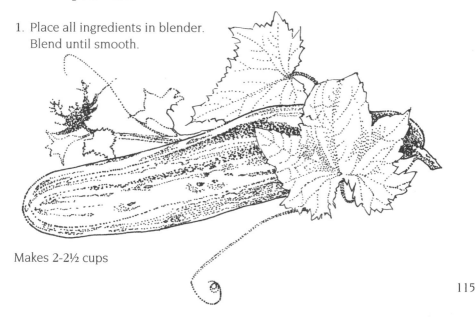

Makes 2-2½ cups

Lemon Ginger Dressing

1	cup olive oil
½	cup lemon juice
½	cup drinking water
1	medium knob ginger, grated or 2 tsp. ground ginger
2	cloves garlic, peeled
2	tbsp. scallions, chopped
1	tsp. dry mustard
1	tsp. tarragon

1. Place all ingredients in a blender. Blend until smooth.

Makes 2 cups

Green Goddess Dressing

¾	cup eggless mayonnaise or San Pasqual mayonnaise
¾	cup fresh parsley
1	tbsp. onion, chopped finely
1	clove garlic
½	tsp. kelp and/or sea salt

1. Place all ingredients in blender. Blend until smooth. Thin with 1 tbsp. of drinking water if desired.

Makes 1½ cups

Celery Dressing

1	large lemon, juiced
½	cup olive oil
1	tbsp. chives, chopped finely
¼	tsp. celery seed
¼	tsp. marjoram
⅛	tsp. garlic powder

1. Whisk ingredients together until well emulsified.

Makes 3/4 cup

SAN PASQUAL MAYONNAISE

3   San Pasqual egg yolks
2   tbsp. apple cider vinegar
1   tsp. dry mustard, ground
½   tsp. sea salt
1½ cups cold pressed safflower oil

1. Beat eggs with whisk or in a food processor or in blender until light and lemon colored. Add vinegar, mustard and salt.
2. Beat in oil drop by drop until it begins to thicken. Continue pouring in a steady stream, beating until all the oil is well incorporated.

Makes 2 cups

EGGLESS MAYONNAISE I

2   tbsp. olive oil
¼   cup lemon juice
½   tsp. dry mustard
8   oz. soft tofu

1. Place all ingredients except tofu in blender. Blend, slowly adding tofu piece by piece, blending smooth with each addition. You may place all ingredients in food processor and blend until smooth.

Makes 1½ cups

EGGLESS MAYONNAISE II

¼   cup lemon juice
2   tbsp. tahini
1   clove garlic
½   tsp. dry mustard
¼   tsp. sea salt
¾   cup olive oil

117

1. Place lemon juice, tahini, garlic, mustard and salt in blender or food processor. Very slowly add oil until emulsified. Chill.

Makes 1 cup

FRENCH DRESSING

1	cup tomatoes, peeled and seeded
¼	cup olive oil
1	tbsp. lemon juice
1	clove garlic
½	tsp. dry mustard
½	tsp. sea salt
¼	tsp. kelp
¼	tsp. black pepper

1. Blend all ingredients together until smooth.

Makes 1¼ cups

PAPAYA MANGO SALSA

1	cup ripe papaya, diced in 1/2 inch cubes
1	cup mango, diced in 1/2 inch cubes
½	cup nectarine, diced in 1/2 inch cubes
2	tbsp. chopped mint
3	tbsp. lime juice
2	tbsp. olive oil
1	tsp. salt
1	tbsp. finely diced green chilies (optional)

1. Combine all ingredients. Let sit at room temperature for at least 20 minutes prior to serving to blend flavors.

Makes 2½ cups

Moroccan Lemon and Olive Salsa

8-10	Mediterranean black olives, pitted and coarsely chopped
8-10	Mediterranean green olives, pitted and coarsely chopped
5	cloves garlic, chopped
½	lemon or lime, finely chopped
3	tbsp. cilantro, finely chopped
2	tsp. ground cumin
2	tsp. paprika
½	tsp. red pepper flakes (optional)
⅓	cup lemon juice
¼	cup olive oil
2	tbsp. water

1. Combine all ingredients, stirring in just enough water to get consistency you desire.

Makes 1 cup

Guacamole

4	large avocados, peeled and seeded
1	large tomato, seeded and diced
½	small red onion, chopped finely
2	cloves garlic, peeled and mashed
2	tbsp. lemon juice
2	tbsp. cilantro, finely chopped
1	tsp. spike
1	tsp. chili powder
½	tsp. oregano

1. Mash avocados with a fork until almost smooth. Mix in other ingredients.

Makes 2 to 2½ cups

SALSA MEXICANO

4   large tomatoes, peeled and diced
1   large onion, finely chopped
3   green onions with tops, sliced thinly
2   cloves garlic, peeled and mashed
2   fresh green chilies, seeded and diced
1   tbsp. cider vinegar
1   tbsp. olive oil
1   tsp. cumin
½   tsp. sea salt
½   tsp. black pepper

1. Mix all ingredients together. Let sit for 20 minutes to blend flavors.

Makes 2 cups

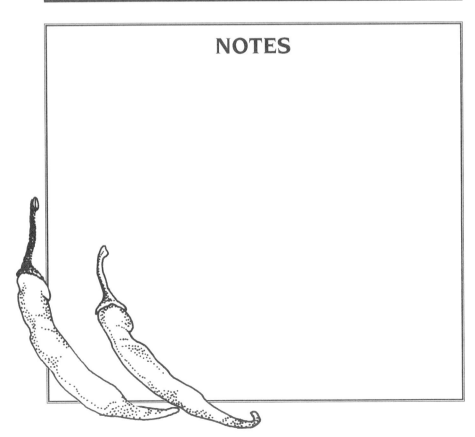

NOTES

SOUPS

SOUPS
VEGETABLES, GRAINS AND FRUITS

Next to raw fruit and vegetable juices, soups are the most easily digestible nutrition. Apart from the nutritional benefits, a bowl of soup can boost the spirit by evoking pleasant memories of childhood when one is feeling a bit below par. Originally, soup was a basic sustenance--a daily pot of warming nourishment that brought the family together around the hearth where it was made. In fact, the first eating establishment ever to be called a restaurant was opened by M. Boulanger in 1756 and served soups exclusively. Above the restaurant door the Latin verse, "Venite ad me omnes qui stomacho laboratis et ego restaurabo"--"Come to me all of you whose stomachs cry out and I will restore you." The word "restaurant" comes from the French *restaurer*, which comes from the Latin *restaurare*, meaning "to restore," and still refers to the restoration of one's well being through the ingestion of soup!

Soup, whether thick and filling or clear and light, should have a place in our everyday cuisine. A bowl of fresh soup can serve as a perfect fall or winter luncheon, or as a light supper during the spring and summer months, each bowlful laden with goodness and nutrition. Canned and prepackaged dehydrated soups are laden with artificial sweeteners, salt, meat stocks and vegetables that have lost almost all their nutritional values.

Just as when purchasing vegetables for juices, when you buy ingredients for soups remember to begin with the freshest, naturally grown products you can find. A good source for fresh produce is your local Farmers's Market or your health food store. These are also good sources for dried legumes and grains that have not been treated with pesticides or debearded. Debearding strips grains of important nutrients and fibers.

Remember to scrub and wash produce well before using.

When making soups, use purified drinking water as chemical contaminents form "tap water" sources may detract form the healthfulness of your final dish.

We have included two recipes for vegetable stock. *Vegetable Stock* I makes a lightly colored and delicately flavored broth while *Vegetable Stock* II is more robust and darkly rich resembling a meat broth. If you do not have time to make stock there are currently several brands of salt-free, natural vegetable stocks in markets today. You may also substitute drinking water flavored with a natural vegetable bouillon in any recipe.

We hope you'll try many of the soups included in this section, including some of the fruit soups which may be new to your palate. We think you will find them a delightful addition to eating healthy food as second nature.

WHITE NAVY BEAN SOUP

2½   cups white navy beans
10   cups fresh drinking water
2   medium carrots, finely chopped
1   large onion, diced
2   stalks celery, finely chopped
2   cloves fresh garlic chopped or 1 tsp. garlic powder
2   tsp. sea salt
2   tsp. ground coriander
½   tsp. curry powder
½   tsp. black pepper
2   cups spinach, roughly chopped
½   cup whipping cream

1. Wash and pick through beans to remove any pebbles or debris. Soak overnight or for 6 hours in 4 cups of the water. Drain water and rinse.

2. Place beans in a non-corrosive, heavy pot. Add the additional 6 cups of water along with carrots, onion, celery, garlic and spices. Bring to a boil. Reduce heat to a simmer and cook for 2½ hours until beans are tender. Add more water if necessary to maintain soup consistency.

3. Add chopped spinach and cream during last 5 minutes of cooking time. Serve hot with crusty whole wheat bread or bread sticks.

Serves 8-10

SCALLION SPINACH SOUP

1   bunch scallions with tops, cut into 1" pieces
1   tbsp. butter
3   medium russet potatoes, diced with skins on
4   cups vegetable stock I
8   cups spinach, washed and chopped
1   cup cream
2   tsp. black pepper
2   tsp. sea salt

1. In a large pot over medium heat, saute scallions in butter until translucent. Add potatoes and broth to cover. You may have to add a little water. Cook until potatoes are very tender. Add spinach and simmer until wilted.

2. Puree spinach mixture. Add cream, salt and pepper. If soup is too thick, add additional broth to thin.

Serves 4-6

QUICK MINESTRONE SOUP

¼	cup olive oil
1	large green bell pepper, chopped
1	large onion, chopped
3	cloves fresh garlic, chopped
2	tsp. basil
2	tsp. oregano leaves
½	tsp. cayenne pepper
1	tsp. vegesal
1	medium carrot, finely diced
1	cup garbanzo beans, cooked
1	cup kidney beans, cooked
2	cups crushed tomatoes
4	cups drinking water
1	cup whole grain pasta
½	cup mushrooms, sliced

1. Heat olive oil in large skillet over medium heat. Add chopped pepper, onion and garlic. Saute until limp but not browned. Add spices and carrot and continue to simmer for 2 minutes. Transfer to a soup pot.

2. Add garbanzo beans, kidney beans, tomatoes and water. Cook over medium heat for 15 minutes to incorporate flavors and soften vegetables.

3. Add dried pasta and mushrooms. Continue cooking for 20 minutes or until pasta is tender. Correct seasonings.

   Like all minestrone soups, this soup is fuller in flavor on the second day. Serve with garlic bread and a green salad with Italian dressing or a simple vinaigrette.

Serves 4-6

ZUKE SOUP

½   medium yellow onion, chopped
2   stalks celery, thinly sliced
2   tbsp. olive oil
¾   cup split peas, rinsed
6   cups vegetable stock II
6   cups zucchini, diced
1   clove garlic, minced
½   tsp. dried basil
½   tsp. black pepper
1   tsp. sea salt
1   lb. spinach, washed and shredded
¼   cup fresh parsley, chopped

1. In a large pot over medium heat, saute onion and celery in oil until translucent. Add split peas and 4 cups of stock. Bring to boil, then simmer for 30 minutes over low heat.

2. Add zucchini, remaining 2 cups of stock, garlic, basil, salt and pepper. Continue cooking for 10 minutes. Puree in blender or food processor. Return to pot.

3. Add spinach and parsley. Continue to cook for 5-7 minutes until spinach is wilted. Adjust seasonings and serve warm.

Serves 6

MISO SOUP

½   cup dry wakame or dulse seaweed
1   cup cabbage, thinly shredded
1   medium carrot, sliced thinly on the diagonal
1   medium yellow onion, sliced thinly
1   lb. spinach, thinly shredded
3   cups water
2   tbsp. olive oil
1   tbsp. miso paste (or to taste)

1. Soak seaweed for 15 minutes in 1 cup of water. Cut into small pieces.

2. Meanwhile, prepare other vegetables. Saute cabbage, carrot and onion in oil for 5 minutes only.

3. Add remaining 2 cups water and seaweed. Simmer for 20 minutes. Dilute miso with small amount of broth. Stir into soup, mix well and serve.

Serves 4

CAULIFLOWER SOUP

1	**small yellow onion, finely chopped**
1	**clove garlic**
2	**tbsp. olive oil**
1	**cup celery, chopped**
2	**medium potatoes, peeled and diced**
4	**cups vegetable stock I**
1	**head cauliflower, cut in florets**
2	**tbsp. fresh basil**
½	**cup red bell pepper, diced (optional)**
1	**tsp. tamari**
1	**tsp. sea salt**
1	**tsp. white pepper**

1. In a large sauce pan, saute onion and garlic in oil over medium heat until translucent. Add celery. Continue cooking until celery is soft. Add potatoes and stock. Cover and cook over low heat until potatoes are very tender.

2. Add cauliflower florets. Continue cooking until tender. Puree small batches in a blender until very smooth. Return to sauce pan.

3. Gently reheat creamed soup. Add basil and red peppers, tamari, salt and pepper. Cook for 1-2 minutes to warm through and serve.

Serves 4-6

CREAM OF ASPARAGUS SOUP

1	bunch scallions, sliced in to 1" pieces
2	tbsp. butter
1	medium russet potato, peeled and finely diced
2	cups vegetable stock I
1	tsp. sea salt
½	tsp. black pepper
2	lb. fresh asparagus
1	cup cream
½	tsp. freshly ground nutmeg

1. Saute scallions in butter in a large sauce pan over medium heat. Add potato with 1 cup of vegetable broth, salt and pepper. Cook until potato is very soft.

2. While potato/onion mixture is cooking, wash asparagus and snap off tough ends. Peel spears, then slice on 1 inch diagonal. Reserve the tips for finishing the soup.

3. Add the asparagus slices and the remaining stock to the well cooked potato mixture. Cook for 10-12 minutes over medium heat until the asparagus is tender. Puree the mixture in small batches to insure a smooth consistency. Replace in pan.

4. Add cream and gently reheat. Add the reserved asparagus tips and nutmeg. Continue cooking over very low heat for 3-5 minutes. Adjust seasonings and serve.

Serves 4

VICHYSSOISE

4	tbsp. butter
2	large leeks, white parts only, chopped
1	small onion, chopped
¼	cup celery, chopped
4	cups vegetable broth I
3	cups potatoes, peeled and thinly sliced
1	cup cream
1	tbsp. sea salt
2	tsp. white pepper
2	tbsp. chives, finely cut

1. Melt butter in a large heavy skillet. Add leeks, onion and celery. Cook over very low heat for about 20 minutes stirring occasionally to insure that vegetables do not color.

2. When vegetables are translucent, transfer to large sauce pan. Add vegetable broth and potatoes. Cover and simmer until potatoes easily fall apart when pierced with a fork.

3. Puree soup through a coarse sieve or food mill. Do not use a blender. Set mixture in a covered bowl in refrigerator to chill at least two hours.

4. When potato mixture is thoroughly chilled, slowly add cream to blend. Adjust seasonings.

5. Place individual servings in bowls. Garnish with finely cut chives.

Serves 4-6

CUCUMBER AND CREAM SOUP

1   large cucumber, peeled, seeded and cut into pieces
2   small dill pickles, cut into pieces
3   tbsp. lemon juice
3   tbsp. grated onion
1   cup cream
1   tbsp. fresh dill, finely cut
1   tsp. sea salt
1   tsp. white pepper
1   small cucumber, finely diced

1. Blend cucumber pieces in blender with pickles, lemon juice and onion until smooth.

2. Pour mixture into a tureen. Stir in cream, dill, salt and pepper. Chill for at least 15 minutes to allow flavors to blend.

3. Place individual servings in bowls. Garnish with diced cucumber and serve immediately.

Serves 2

5 MINUTE BLACK BEAN SOUP

2	15 oz. cans black beans
1	medium yellow onion, finely diced
2	tbsp. olive oil
2	cloves garlic, minced
1	tbsp. tamari
½	tsp. ground cumin
1	tsp. salt
½	tsp. cayenne pepper
1	15 oz. can vegetable stock
2	cups water
2	limes, quartered
¼	cup cilantro, washed and chopped

1. Rinse canned beans in a colander. Set aside.

2. In a large sauce pan, saute onion in oil over medium heat until translucent. Add garlic, tamari and spices. Continue to cook for 1 minute. Add beans, stock and water and one lime. Cook over medium heat until mixture reaches a boil. Remove lime.

3. Puree one half of mixture then return and stir until well blended. Serve with remaining lime and cilantro as a garnish.

Serves 4

NOTES

GAZPACHO

4	large tomatoes, diced and seeded
1	medium cucumber, diced finely
½	small red onion, chopped finely
½	medium red pepper, chopped finely
1	large ripe avocado, diced
2	cups vegetable stock II
¼	cup olive oil
2	tbsp. lemon juice
1	clove garlic, minced
1	tsp. kelp
2	tbsp. cilantro or parsley, finely chopped

1. Mix all ingredients in a bowl. Set in refrigerator to chill for at least 30 minutes.

OPTION: Add 1 cup homemade tomato juice to ingredients before chilling.

Serves 2-4

MINTED FRESH PEA SOUP

1	lb. frozen petite peas
2	cups vegetable broth I
2	cups cream
1	tsp. sea salt
1	tsp. white pepper
¼	cup fresh mint, thinly shredded

1. Puree peas in food processor with 1 cup vegetable broth and 1 cup cream until smooth.

2. Transfer to tureen. Add remaining broth, cream, salt and pepper. Stir in fresh mint. Serve immediately or hold for up to three hours in refrigerator.

Serves 4

POTATO SOUP WITH TOMATOES AND BASIL

3	large tomatoes
2	carrots, thinly sliced
1	tbsp. sea salt
2	tsp. black pepper
2	cups vegetable broth I
4	medium russet potatoes, diced
1	large onion, sliced
1	clove garlic, minced
1	cup cream
¼	cup fresh basil leaves, finely shredded

1. Cut tomatoes in half crosswise to remove seeds. Reserve juice. Finely chop tomatoes. Place chopped tomatoes, reserved juice, carrots, salt and pepper in an enameled sauce pan over medium heat. When mixture begins to bubble, lower heat and simmer until carrots are soft. Puree should be dense like a tomato sauce for pasta. Increase heat to boil off extra liquid. Pass puree through a strainer to remove tomato skins and chill.

2. Place vegetable broth, potatoes, onion and garlic into a medium sauce pan. Simmer for 15-20 minutes until potatoes are very tender and onion is soft. Puree mixture in a blender. Add cream, season to taste and chill in a tureen.

3. When ready to serve, swirl tomato puree into the potato soup. Garnish with finely shredded basil leaves.

Serves 4

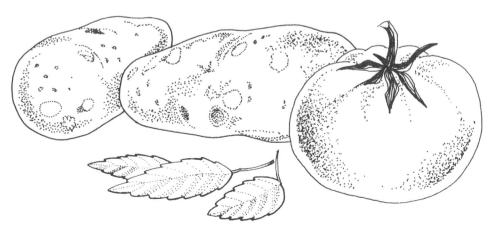

CREAM OF AVOCADO SOUP

1	large ripe avocado, peeled and pitted
¼	cup fresh squeezed lemon juice
¼	cup fresh squeezed lime juice
1½	cups vegetable stock I
¾	cup cream
¼	cup cilantro, finely chopped
1	tsp. sea salt
1	tsp. pepper

1. Mash avocado into lemon and lime juice with a fork leaving the pulp to remain in pieces about the size of a pea.

2. Place mixture in a medium sized enamel coated sauce pan over low heat. Slowly add vegetable broth, stirring to blend, then follow with cream. Bring soup to a boil and simmer for 2 minutes.

3. Serve hot or chill and serve cold. Once each serving is placed in the bowl, garnish with fresh cilantro.

Serves 2

CREAM OF MUSHROOM SOUP

¼	oz. dried porcini mushrooms
2½	cups fresh mushrooms brushed clean with vegetable brush and, chopped
¼	cup onion, finely chopped
5	cups vegetable stock II
4	tbsp. butter
¼	cup whole wheat pastry flour
1	cup cream
2	tsp. sea salt
2	tsp. black pepper
1	tbsp. fresh thyme, finely chopped
¼	cup sauterne or other sweet white wine (optional)

1. In a small bowl, place porcini mushrooms. Pour just enough boiling water over to cover. Let sit 15 minutes to soften. Strain soaking liquid through very fine strainer and reserve. Chop mushrooms finely.

2. Place fresh mushrooms and onion in stock. Simmer for 20 minutes. Pass vegetables and stock through a sieve. Place back on burner over low constant heat adding porcini mushrooms and the reserved liquid.

3. Work butter and flour together to make a paste. Whisk into the gently simmering soup to thicken. Add cream, salt, pepper and fresh thyme. Heat for 5 more minutes. Add wine just prior to serving.

Serves 6

CHILLED WATERCRESS PEAR SOUP

8	ripe pears
2	cups apple juice
2	cups drinking water
2	bunches watercress, leaves and stems chopped except for 12 leaves left whole
2	tbsp. lemon juice
1	tsp. sea salt
1	tsp. black pepper
¾	cup cream

1. Peel, core and quarter pears reserving skins and peels. Plunge pears into apple juice immediately to prevent discoloration.

2. Boil skins and cores in drinking water for 5 minutes to extract flavor, then strain into larger, enamel coated sauce pan. Add chopped watercress to broth, then simmer for 10 minutes. Puree the mixture in a blender or food mill.

3. Puree pear quarters with the apple juice in a blender then combine the two mixtures. Add lemon juice and salt and pepper. Chill thoroughly.

4. Just before serving, add cream. Adjust seasoning. Place in tureen and float remaining watercress leaves on top.

Serves 4-6

Malagan Garlic Soup with Grapes

5   cloves garlic
2   tbsp. ground almonds or 30 fresh almonds
⅓   cup brown bread crumbs
1   tbsp. sea salt
2   tbsp. olive oil
1   tbsp. vinegar
2   cups drinking water
1   lb. green grapes, peeled and halved
6   ice cubes

1. Grind garlic, almonds, bread crumbs and salt together in a food processor.

2. Gradually add oil, mixing well. Add vinegar and water. Place mixture in tureen.

3. Add grapes and ice. Leave mixture in cool place for 25 minutes then serve. This soup does not hold.

Serves 2-4

Chilled Split Pea Soup

2   cups dried split peas
6   cups vegetable broth II
½   cup celery, finely chopped
1   bay leaf
1   tbsp. tamari
2   tsp. pepper
1   cup cream
2   tbsp. fresh thyme
2   tbsp. fresh mint

1. In 5-quart sauce pan combine peas, broth, celery, bay leaf, tamari and pepper. Bring to a vigorous boil over heat. Reduce heat and simmer for 1½ hours until peas can be easily mashed with a fork

2. Remove bay leaf. Puree soup in food processor. Stir in cream, thyme and mint. Chill for at least 2 hours. After chilling, soup will have thickened considerably. You may wish to add more broth or cream to thin consistency. Adjust seasoning and serve

Serves 6

CURRIED RED BEAN SOUP

2	cups red kidney beans, soaked overnight and drained
3½	quarts drinking water
1	bouquet garni composed of 2 whole cloves, 1 bay leaf, 1 small red chile wrapped in cheesecloth
2	medium red potatoes, diced
4	tbsp. butter
1	large onion, chopped
2	tsp. curry
1	tsp. cumin
1	tbsp. tamari
2	tsp. sea salt
2	tsp. black pepper
8	small sour gherkins (optional)
	croutons

1. Place beans in large soup pot. Add water and bouquet garni. Slowly bring to boil for 10 minutes. Reduce heat, simmering for 1 hour more.

2. Add potatoes and continue cooking for 30 minutes.

3. Meanwhile, heat butter in skillet. Add onions, curry, cumin and tamari. Cook over medium heat until onion is translucent. Add to soup pot along with salt and pepper.

4. Continue cooking 20 minutes more until soup thickens. Adjust seasoning, removing bouquet garni. Add sliced gherkins. Serve hot with croutons.

Serves 10

RUSSIAN BORSCHT

1½ lb. fresh beets, leaves removed and saved
4   tbsp. butter
1   tsp. sea salt
1   tsp. pepper
2   tbsp. malt vinegar
1   cup heavy cream
1   medium onion, diced
1   rib celery, thinly sliced on diagonal
½   head green cabbage, finely shredded
1   bouquet garni composed of 1 bay leaf, 6 pepper
    corns, 2 sprigs marjoram, 3 sprigs fresh thyme
    wrapped in cheesecloth
3   medium potatoes, diced
6   cups drinking water
2   tbsp. chives, finely chopped

1. Wrap beets in a double layer of aluminum foil. Dot with 1 tbsp. butter, sprinkle with salt and pepper. Bake at 400° for 1 hour or until beets are tender when pierced with a fork.

2. Mix one tbsp. of vinegar into cream. Let sit at room temperature. Meanwhile, saute onion, celery and cabbage using remaining butter in a large soup pot.

4. When beets have cooled enough to handle, peel tough skin and dice. Place beets, reserved beet greens and bouquet garni in soup pot with potatoes and cabbage/onion mixture. Add water and vinegar. Cook for 45 minutes until potatoes are tender.

5. Serve with soured cream and chives as garnish.

Serves 6-8

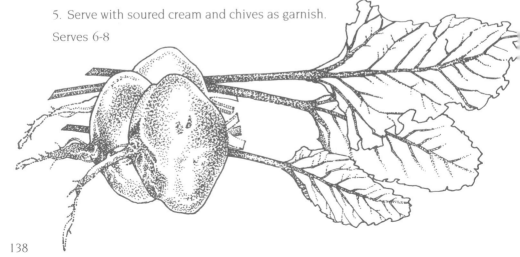

MOROCCAN LENTIL SOUP

4	tbsp. olive oil
1	medium onion, finely chopped
2	medium carrots, thinly sliced on diagonal
2	ribs celery, thinly sliced on diagonal
1	tsp. ground cinnamon
½	tsp. ground cloves
½	tsp. curry powder
2	tsp. sea salt
2	tsp. pepper
2	cups lentils
1	15 oz. can plum tomatoes
2	cups fresh tomato juice
1	tbsp. malt barley sweetener
4	cups drinking water
3	tbsp. lemon juice

1. Heat oil in a large soup pot. Add onions, carrots, celery and spices. Cook over medium heat until onions are translucent.

2. Add lentils, tomatoes, tomato juice, sweetener and water. Bring mixture to a boil. Simmer over low heat until lentils are tender, 30 to 45 minutes. Add lemon juice. Adjust seasonings.

Serves 6

CHILLED CANTALOUPE SOUP

1	3 lb. cantaloupe, seeded and removed from shell
¼	cup raw honey
½	cup dry, white wine or white grape juice
1	tbsp. lime juice

1. Combine all ingredients in a blender until very smooth. Chill for at least 3 hours. Serve very cold.

Serves 2

VEGETABLE BARLEY PUREE

¼ cup barley

⅓ cup white beans, boiled for 10 minutes or soaked overnight

4 medium carrots, thinly sliced on diagonal

3 leeks, washed and thinly sliced

1 small turnip, diced

1 rib celery, thinly sliced on diagonal

1 medium potato, diced

1 small onion stuck with 3 whole cloves

12 cups drinking water

1 bouquet garni composed of 1 bay leaf, 6 pepper corns, 2 sprigs marjoram, 3 sprigs fresh thyme wrapped in cheesecloth

½ cup butter

1. Place all ingredients except butter into a large, heavy sauce pan. Simmer gently for 3 hours.

2. Remove bouquet garni. Puree through coarse sieve. Place in tureen and add butter. Swirl butter throughout soup and serve.

Serves 8-10

AVOCADO TOMATO SOUP

5 large ripe tomatoes, diced

2 large ripe avocados, diced

3 scallions, sliced thinly

¼ cup almonds, ground

1 cup vegetable broth I

1 tsp. kelp or sea salt

1 lemon, juiced

1. Combine all ingredients.

2. Serve either chilled or heated to just below 115°.

Serves 2-4

WINTER SQUASH AND CHARD SOUP

6	cups winter squash, cubed (if raw) <u>OR</u>
4	cups winter squash, cubed (if cooked)
1	large yellow onion, diced
2	tbsp. butter
½	cup parsley, washed and chopped
2	tsp. sea salt
½	tsp. cinnamon
½	tsp. cumin
½	tsp. black pepper
3	cups water
4	cups chard, devained and finely shredded
½	cup cream

1. If you are not using left over baked squash, then place squash in a large sauce pan. Cover with water and simmer until the squash is soft. Reserve 3 cups of cooking liquid and omit water from recipe.

2. Saute onion in butter over medium heat until translucent. Add parsley and spices. Cook 1-2 minutes longer until parsley is soft.

3. Combine the onion mixture with squash and either the cooking liquid or water from above ingredients. Gently heat. Do not boil or the soup will stick.

4. Stir in the chard and continue heating until the chard has wilted. Add cream, correct seasoning and serve.

Serves 6

NOTES

CHRISTMAS CHESTNUT SOUP

2½   lb. chestnuts
3   quarts vegetable stock I
2   cups cream
1   tsp. salt
½   tsp. cayenne
1   tbsp. barley malt sweetener

1. Slash chestnuts on the flat end with a sharp paring knife. Parboil chestnuts for 10 minutes in boiling water then drain. When cool enough to handle, slip off inner and outer skins. If they do not slip off easily, reheat chestnut.

2. Place chestnuts in large soup pot just covered with stock. Simmer slowly for 40 minutes or until soft. Remove chestnuts, reserving the liquid. Pound chestnuts smooth with a mortar or food mill.

3. Very gradually, while stirring constantly, add the chestnuts back into the stock. Slowly add remaining stock, cream, salt, cayenne and barley sweetener. Bring to boil once. Serve immediately.

Serves 10

CARROT SOUP WITH PEPPERS

4   large red bell peppers
1   large onion, diced
2   tbsp. olive oil
4   medium carrots, diced
1   medium potato, diced
4   cups vegetable broth I
¾   cup cream
1   tbsp. grated lemon peel
½   tbsp. fresh thyme, finely chopped

1. Roast peppers over open flame if you have a gas stove until skin blisters. Immediately place in a paper bag then place that bag into a plastic bag. Let sit for 10 minutes, then peel. If you do not have a gas stove, place peppers on a lightly oiled baking pan and roast in oven at 450° for 12 minutes, then follow the same procedure as above after removal from the oven. When peppers are cooled, remove skin and seeds.

2. While peppers are cooling, saute onion in olive oil until translucent. Add carrots, potatoes, and stock. Cover pan and cook over medium heat for 15 minutes or until carrots and potatoes are very tender.

3. Place peppers and carrot mixture into blender. Blend until smooth. Add cream and lemon peel. Reheat until just boiling. Remove from heat and pour into tureen. Place soup in individual bowls, garnish with fresh thyme.

Serves 4

FRUIT GAZPACHO

½	**cup strawberries, sliced**
1	**cup grapes, sliced**
½	**cup oranges, sliced with white underpeel intact**
1	**cup mango, diced**
½	**cup blueberries**
1	**cup fresh apple juice**
½	**cup orange juice**
2	**tbsp. lime juice**
¼	**tsp. black pepper**
12	**fresh mint leaves**

1. Combine all fruits with juices and pepper in noncorrosive bowl. Chill thoroughly. Serve with fresh mint garnish.

Serves 4

EGGPLANT SOUP

2	tbsp. olive oil
1	small onion, diced
1	rib celery, thinly sliced
1	leek, thinly sliced
2	medium eggplants, peeled and cubed
2	medium white potatoes, diced
3	cups vegetable stock II
1	tsp. tamari
1	tsp. sea salt
1	tsp. pepper
⅓	cup chickpeas, cooked
2	tbsp. tahini
½	cup cream
½	cup apple juice
2	tsp. orange peel

1. Heat oil in large skillet. Saute onion, celery and leeks until softened but not browned. Transfer to soup pot.

2. Add eggplant, potatoes, vegetable stock, tamari, salt and pepper. Cook over medium heat for 20 minutes or until potatoes are tender. Remove from heat.

3. Place eggplant mixture, chickpeas and tahini in blender. Blend until smooth. Transfer back to soup pot. Add cream and apple juice. Cook over low heat until heated through. Add orange peel and serve.

Serves 4

RAW GREEN SOUP

1/2	cup parsley, finely chopped
1/2	cup celery with tops, finely chopped
1/2	cup spinach leaves, finely chopped
1/2	cup mild leaf lettuce, finely chopped
2	cups boiling drinking water
2	tsp. vegetable bouillon
1	tsp. kelp
	butter (optional)

1. Blend all ingredients in blender. Serve immediately with a pat of butter if desired.

Serves 2

VEGETABLE STOCK I

2   medium leeks, washed and chopped
4   medium onion chopped with skins left on
6   carrots, scrubbed and chopped
4   ribs celery with tops, chopped
1   small bunch parsley, chopped
2   bay leaves
2   tsp. dried leaf marjoram
1   tsp. fresh thyme
1½ gallons drinking water

1. Combine all ingredients in large stock pot. Bring to a boil. Reduce heat and simmer 1 hour.

2. Cover a colander or strainer with a double liner of cheesecloth. Strain stock through cheesecloth. Cool completely. Refrigerate or store in freezer to keep longer than two days.

Makes 10 quarts

VEGETABLE STOCK II

4   large onions, halved with skins intact
6   large carrots, scrubbed
1   bunch celery with tops intact
2   tbsp. olive oil
1½ gallons drinking water
1   bunch parsley stems
3   bay leaves
1   tbsp. fresh thyme

1. Place onions, carrots and celery in baking pan. Dribble with olive oil. Roast in 400° oven for 45 minutes until vegetables are well darkened.

2. Transfer vegetables to stock pot. Cover with water. Add parsley stems, bay leaves and thyme. Bring mixture to boil, then simmer for 1 hour.

3. Cover a colander or strainer with a double liner of cheesecloth. Strain stock through cheesecloth. Cool completely. Refrigerate or store in freezer to keep longer than two days.

Makes 10 quarts

PASTA

PASTA

Noodles, Fresh Vegetables and Sauces

Whether you believe pasta in the form of noodles was first brought to Europe from China by Marco Polo, or invented by the Italians themselves, none can deny the fundamental attraction of pasta as an easy, tasty, fat-free food that lends itself to all sorts of variations both in shapes and saucy complements. The truth is, ravioli was being eaten in Rome in 1284, according to the research of globe-trotting chef Mary Luisa Scott, twenty years before Marco Polo's famous travels began. She also points out that museum documents confirm that pasta was being consumed as far back as 5,000 B.C. Draw your own conclusions.

While the word "pasta" simply indicates the generic form of the multitude of products made from semolina and water, it is the semolina itself that lends both the substance and nutrition to a pasta dish. Semolina is the fine flour made from the heart of durum wheat, hence the best pasta requires 100% pure durum as its base. Whole grain pastas are readily available and may be used in any recipe calling for white flour pastas, giving all the advantages of unrefined nutrients.

Pasta noodles made from durum are a golden yellow. They keep their shape when boiled and, when prepared properly, are tender and pliable. The Italians prepare their pasta "al dente," which means the pasta is still slightly hard when pressed between the teeth. At this stage, the pasta has its full flavor and sauce or oil will cling to it easily.

Red wheat pastas are also commonly available. These pastas are brownish in color and have a definite "chew" when prepared. Buckwheat noodles have a more assertive flavor and are very fragile. Soba is a type of buckwheat noodle that is available in most oriental markets. Any of these pastas may be used in most of these recipes.

We have included many recipes that call for sauce that isn't cooked. That is, the ingredients are mixed together and left to blend flavors at room temperature. Don't worry about the sauce not being hot when served. The heat from the freshly cooked noodles warms the sauce to a perfect temperature ready for the table. Other recipes include heavier sauces that may be most appropriate for cool weather and rely on vegetables more suited to that time of year.

Each recipe has been selected to be made with one pound of dried pasta. Shapes may be interchanged at will. You can substitute rigatoni (grooved tubes) for farfalle ("bows"), or mostaccioli for fusilli (corkscrews), or vermicelli (thin noodles) for fettucine (wide noodles) -- it doesn't matter. The only difference may be a different cooking time for each shape, but you'll learn quickly how long to boil each one.

The recommendations made in each recipe are for those we feel hold the sauce best. The sauces are also excellent served over baked potatoes, brown rice, lentils or a variety of other legumes.

Pasta sauces are a great way to add variety to your meal planning. As always, each sauce relies on the freshest produce, the most healthful additions, and whole grain pastas. Herbs and spices have been chosen to enhance flavors, but feel free to adjust seasoning to your own palate.

Serve pasta either as a first course or as an entree. Whichever, we hope you will find these recipes an exciting addition to your new style of eating.

And as the Italians would say, "*Buon Apetito!*"

PASTA FRESCA

1	pound whole wheat spaghetti
1	yellow onion, chopped
2	cloves garlic, minced
1½	pounds ripe tomatoes, peeled, seeded and chopped
2	tbsp. olive paste (available at specialty food stores)
½	cup fresh basil, thinly sliced
1	tsp. sea salt
1	tsp. black pepper

1. Bring 4 quarts of water with 1 tbsp. sea salt to boil in a large pot and cook pasta according to directions on package. Do not over cook. It should be firm to the bite.

2. Meanwhile, heat oil in large skillet. Add onions and saute until translucent. Add garlic and tomatoes. Simmer over medium heat until liquid from tomatoes is reduced by one half. Add olive paste and basil, salt and pepper.

3. Drain pasta. Toss with tomato sauce and serve immediately.

Serves 4-6

PASTA VERDE

1	lb. buckwheat noodles
2	cloves garlic, peeled and mashed
6	green onions, sliced
1	lb. fresh spinach, washed and stemmed
1	bunch broccoli, cut in flowerets
2	tbsp. fresh basil, finely chopped
¼	cup Italian parsley, finely chopped
½	tsp. nutmeg
1	tsp. sea salt
1	tsp. black pepper
4	oz. soft tofu
½	tsp. dry mustard

1. Bring 4 quarts of water and 1 tbsp. of sea salt to boil in a large pot. Add pasta and cook according to directions on package. Do not over cook. Buckwheat noodles are very fragile. Drain, reserving 1/2 cup of cooking liquid.

2. Meanwhile, place olive oil, garlic and green onions in a large saute pan. Cook over low heat 3-5 minutes until onions have wilted and garlic is fragrant but not browned. Add spinach and broccoli. Toss vegetables to coat with oil. Cover and steam for 5-7 minutes. Uncover pan and stir in basil, parsley, nutmeg, salt and pepper.

3. Place tofu and dry mustard in blender. Blend until smooth. Add vegetables. Continue to blend for 1-2 minutes.

4. Add hot cooking liquid to sauce in blender. Place noodles in a shallow serving bowl. Very gently, toss with sauce and serve.

Serves 4-6

TUBETTI WITH TOMATO AND AVOCADO SAUCE

12	basil leaves, torn into fragments
1	tsp. cilantro, finely chopped
1	clove garlic, peeled and mashed
½	cup extra virgin olive oil
1	lemon, cut in half
1	tsp. sea salt
1	tsp. black pepper
1	lb. whole wheat tubetti or other whole wheat tube pasta
1	large avocado

1. Combine tomatoes, basil, cilantro and garlic in a small bowl. Add olive oil and the juice of ½ lemon. Season with sea salt and pepper. Let stand for 1 hour.

2 Bring 4 quarts of water and 1 tbsp. sea salt to boil in a large pot. Add pasta and cook according to directions on package. Do not over cook. It should be firm to the bite.

3. While pasta is cooking, peel avocado and cut into a small dice. Place into small bowl and toss gently with remaining lemon juice.

4. Drain pasta. Place in shallow serving bowl and toss with tomato mixture. Spoon avocado and lemon juice over the top and serve.

Serves 4-6

PASTA WITH SUMMER VEGETABLES

1   lb. whole wheat penne or other whole wheat tube pasta
1   small red pepper, cored, seeded and diced
1   small green pepper, cored, seeded and diced
1   large tomato, cored and finely diced
1   rib celery, finely diced
½   small red onion, finely diced
½   medium seedless cucumber, peeled and finely diced
1   small carrot, scrubbed and finely chopped
1   small zucchini, finely diced
½   cup extra virgin olive oil
½   cup basil leaves, torn in fragments
1   tsp. sea salt
1   tsp. freshly ground pepper
¼   cup soy parmesan

1. Combine all vegetables with olive oil, basil, sea salt and pepper in a large serving dish.

2. Bring 4 quarts of water and 1 tbsp. of sea salt to a boil in a large pot. Add pasta and cook according to directions on package. Do not over cook. It should be firm to the bite. Drain well.

3. Toss pasta with raw vegetables, top with parmesan and serve.

Serves 4-6

TAGLIATELLE WITH BROAD BEANS

1   lb. whole wheat tagliatelle or fettuccine
3   tbsp. olive oil
1   medium red onion, chopped
2   lbs. fresh broad beans, shelled and skins removed
1   tsp. sea salt
1   tsp. black pepper
⅔   cup soy parmesan cheese

1. Bring 4 quarts of water and 1 tbsp. of sea salt to boil in a large pot. Add pasta and cook according to directions on package. Do not over cook. It should remain firm to the bite. Drain, reserving ¼ cup of cooking liquid.

2. Meanwhile, place olive oil and onion in large skillet. Cook on low heat 5-7 minutes until onion is translucent but not browned. Add beans, salt and pepper. Cover with just enough water to barely cover beans. With the lid slightly ajar, boil rapidly until almost all of the water has evaporated.

3. Place pasta in a shallow serving bowl. Toss gently with reserved cooking liquid. Toss gently with beans and parmesan. Serve.

Serves 4-6

ARTICHOKE PASTA

1	lb. whole wheat shells
4	medium artichokes
3	tbsp. olive oil
1	tbsp. butter
1	medium onion, thinly sliced
1	clove garlic, peeled and mashed
2	cups canned Italian plum tomatoes
1	bay leaf
1	tbsp. fresh basil, chopped
1	tsp. salt
1	tsp. pepper

1. Remove all tough outer leaves of artichokes. Trim and slice in half. Remove choke, then thinly slice artichoke halves lengthwise.

2. Heat oil and butter in a large skillet add artichokes, cook stirring constantly for 3 minutes. Add onion, garlic, tomatoes, bay leaf, basil, salt and pepper. Reduce heat to low and simmer for 25 minutes, stirring occasionally, until artichokes are tender.

3. While sauce simmers, bring 4 quarts of water and 1 tbsp. of sea salt to boil in a large pot. Add pasta and cook according to directions on package. Do not overcook. It should remain firm to the bite. Drain.

4. Place pasta in shallow serving dish. Toss with sauce and serve.

Serves 4-6

COOL BUCKWHEAT NOODLES WITH CUCUMBERS

½   lb. buckwheat noodles, boiled, drained, rinsed and chilled
½   cup rice vinegar
¼   cup sesame oil
¼   cup soy sauce
2   tbsp. raw honey
1   tsp. fresh ginger, grated
1   clove garlic, peeled and mashed (optional)
½   lb. mushrooms, brushed, trimmed and sliced thinly
2   large cucumbers, peeled, halved, seeded and cut into long shreds
4   scallions, thinly sliced

1. In small sauce pan, heat vinegar, sesame oil, soy sauce, honey, ginger and garlic together, stirring frequently to avoid sticking. Simmer for 5 minutes. Cool.

2. In a medium skillet, poach mushrooms in 2 tbsp. water for 3-5 minutes just to soften slightly and release flavor. Reduce any cooking liquid to 4 tbsp. and add to chilled sauce.

3. Gently place buckwheat noodles in shallow serving dish. Toss with sauce and mushrooms. Gently fold in cucumber shreds. Top with sliced scallions. Serve.

Serves 4-6

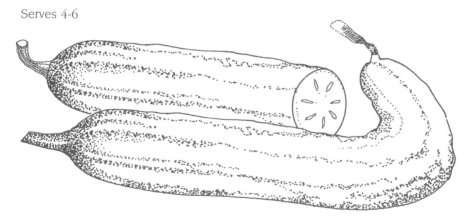

PASTA WITH UNCOOKED TOMATO SAUCE

1	lb. any whole grain pasta
6	medium ripe tomatoes
1	bunch basil, stemmed and chopped
6	cloves garlic, peeled and slightly crushed
¾	cup extra virgin olive oil
1	tsp. sea salt
1	tsp. freshly ground black pepper

1. Bring a medium pan of water to boil. Drop tomatoes into boiling water for 1-2 minutes until skins split. Core, peel and seed tomatoes. Cut into ¼" dice. In medium bowl, mix tomatoes, basil, garlic, olive oil, salt and pepper. Cover and let sit for at least 20 minutes to blend flavors.

2. Meanwhile, bring 4 quarts of water and 1 tbsp. of sea salt to boil in a large pot. Add pasta and cook according to directions on package. Do not over cook. It should remain firm to the bite. Drain.

3. Remove garlic cloves from tomato sauce. Toss with hot pasta. Serve immediately.

Serves 4-6

CAPELLINI WITH MUSHROOMS AND LEMON

1	lb. whole wheat capellini
1	lb. fresh mushrooms
¾	cup olive oil
3	cloves garlic, peeled and mashed
½	cup Italian parsley, finely chopped
1	tsp. sea salt
1	tsp. pepper
1	lemon with peel removed then juiced

1. Wipe mushrooms clean with a damp paper towel and trim ends. Cut mushrooms into thick slices, then cut slices in half.

2. In a medium saute pan, combine olive oil, garlic and parsley. Saute over low heat for 2-3 minutes. Add mushrooms and cook until they begin to release their juices. Season with salt and pepper. Remove from heat. Add lemon juice and lemon peel.

3. Meanwhile, bring 4 quarts of water and 1 tbsp. of sea salt to boil in a large pot. Add pasta and cook according to directions on package. Do not over cook. The fine pasta should remain firm to the bite. Drain, reserving about ½ cup of pasta cooking water.

4. Toss pasta and reserved cooking liquid with sauce. You may wish to grind fresh pepper over the top. Serve.

Serves 4-6

MIXED HERB PASTA

HERB MIXTURE

2	tbsp. fresh parsley, finely chopped
1	tbsp. fresh tarragon, finely chopped
2	tsp. shallots, finely chopped
1	tsp. fresh thyme, finely chopped
1	tsp. fresh sage, finely chopped
1	tsp. fresh rosemary, finely chopped
¾	cup sesame oil
1	tsp. sea salt
1	tsp. black pepper
½	tsp. dry mustard

1	lb. whole wheat fettuccine
2	tbsp. sesame oil
2	tsp. sea salt
4	tbsp. cream

1. Place all herb mixture ingredients in blender. Blend 1 minute to puree.

2. Bring 4 quarts of water, 2 tbsp. of sesame oil and 1 tbsp. of sea salt to boil in large pot. Add pasta and cook according to directions on package. Do not over cook. It should remain firm to the bite. Drain.

3. Place pasta in a shallow serving dish. Coat lightly with cream. Add herb mixture and toss again. Serve.

Serves 4-6

Pasta Primavera

1	lb. spinach fettuccine
½	lb. asparagus
4	tbsp. olive oil
¼	cup yellow onion, finely diced
¼	cup celery, finely diced
½	cup carrots, finely diced
½	cup zucchini, finely diced
¼	cup red pepper, seeded and finely diced
1	cup cream
1	tsp. sea salt
1	tsp. black pepper
2	tbsp. Italian parsley, finely chopped
¼	cup soy parmesan

1. Trim and peel stems of asparagus. Place in boiling water until spears turn bright green but are still crisp. Remove. Cut into ¾ inch lengths on the diagonal.

2. Heat olive oil in a large skillet over medium heat. Add onion and cook 3-5 minutes until translucent. Add celery and carrot. Continue cooking for 5 minutes more.

3. Add zucchini and peppers to skillet. Continue cooking for 10-15 minutes until vegetables are tender. Add asparagus and cook for 1 minute. Add cream, salt and pepper. Continue cooking until cream is reduced by half. Remove from heat and set aside.

4. Meanwhile, bring 4 quarts of water and 1 tbsp. sea salt to boil in a large pot. Add pasta and cook according to directions on package. Do not over cook. It should remain firm to the bite. Drain.

5. Place pasta in shallow serving bowl. Toss with sauce. Top with parsley and cheese.

Serves 4-6

158

Pasta with Sweet Pepper Sauce

1	lb. whole wheat ziti or other whole wheat tube pasta
2	large red peppers
2	large green peppers
1	lb. ripe plum tomatoes or 1-28 oz. can of Italian plum tomatoes, drained
½	cup olive oil
1	medium yellow onion, finely diced
1	clove garlic, peeled and mashed
1	tsp. sea salt
¼	tsp. cayenne pepper
⅓	cup Italian parsley, finely chopped

1. Roast peppers in 450° oven until skin blisters. Place in a bowl, covered tightly with plastic wrap for 15 minutes. Remove skin, cores and seeds. While peppers are cooling, core, peel and seed tomatoes if using fresh. Seed and drain tomatoes if using canned. Puree tomatoes and peppers together in a blender.

2. Place oil and onion in medium saute pan. Cook over low heat until onion is translucent but not brown. Add garlic. Cook 1-2 minutes more. Add pepper puree, salt and cayenne. Continue to cook for 5-6 minutes to blend flavors. Keep warm.

3. Meanwhile, bring 4 quarts of water and 1 tbsp. of sea salt to boil in large pot. Add pasta and cook according to directions on package. Do not over cook. It should remain firm to the bite. Drain.

4. Place pasta in shallow serving bowl. Toss gently with sauce. Add parsley and toss again. Serve.

Serves 4-6

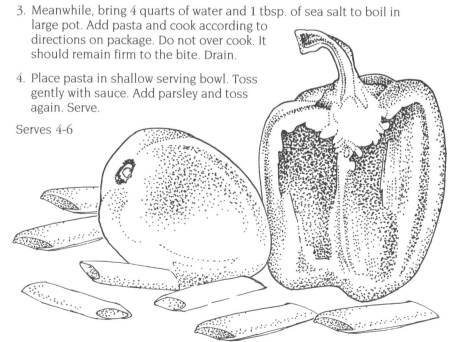

SPINACH SPAGHETTI WITH MUSHROOMS AND CREAM

1	lb. whole wheat spaghetti
6	tbsp. fresh lemon juice
1	lb. mushrooms, wiped, trimmed and sliced
4	tbsp. butter
2	clove garlic, peeled and mashed
2	tbsp. Marsala wine (optional)
2	cups cream
2	lb. spinach, washed and stemmed
1	tsp. salt
1	tsp. black pepper
⅓	cup soy parmesan

1. Mix lemon juice and mushrooms together in medium bowl.

2. Melt butter in a large skillet, add garlic and Marsala. Cook for 3 minutes. Add mushrooms. Cook for 5 minutes more. Add cream and bring mixture to a boil. Stir in spinach to wilt. Add salt and pepper. Remove from heat.

2. Meanwhile, bring 4 quarts of water and 1 tbsp. sea salt to boil in a large pot. Add pasta and cook according to directions on package. Do not over cook. It should remain firm to the bite. Drain.

3. Place pasta in shallow serving bowl. Toss gently with sauce. Serve with cheese on top.

Serves 4-6

NOTES

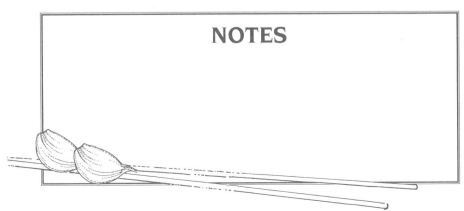

PENNE WITH GOLDEN GARLIC

1 lb. whole wheat penne or other whole wheat tube pasta
½ cup extra virgin olive oil
12 cloves fresh garlic, peeled and lightly crushed
1 28 oz. can Italian plum tomatoes, seeded and coarsely chopped, juice reserved
1 cube vegetable bouillon
1 tsp. sea salt
½ tsp. red pepper flakes
4 tbsp. soy parmesan cheese

1. Place olive oil and garlic in medium saute pan. Cook over medium-low heat 15-18 minutes until garlic is soft and golden in color, stirring frequently to prevent sticking. Add tomatoes, reserved juice, bouillon cube and salt and pepper. Continue cooking 20-25 minutes until sauce has thickened.

2. Meanwhile, bring 4 quarts of water and 1 tbsp. sea salt to boil in a large pot. Add pasta and cook according to package directions. Do not over cook. It should remain firm to the bite. Drain well.

3. Place pasta in a shallow serving bowl. Toss gently with sauce. Sprinkle parmesan over top and serve.

Serves 4-6

SOBA WITH CHINESE MUSHROOMS

6 oz. soba
6 Chinese dried mushrooms
1 tbsp. sesame oil
2 cloves garlic, peeled and sliced
½ lb. zucchini, julienned into 2" shreds
1 tbsp. soy sauce
3 scallions, thinly sliced
2 tbsp. sesame seeds, lightly toasted

1. Soak dried mushrooms in warm water or vegetable stock for 30 minutes. Drain, trim ends and slice thinly.

2. Heat oil in a wok over high heat for 1 minute and add garlic. Stir fry garlic for 5 seconds, then add zucchini and mushrooms. Continue cooking over high heat for 1 minute. Add soba, continue cooking, stirring constantly for 2 minutes. Add soy sauce. Cook 1 minute longer.

3. Place in shallow serving dish. Top with scallions and sesame seeds. Serve.

Serves 4-6

PENNE WITH ZUCCHINI AND CREAM

1	lb. whole wheat penne or other whole wheat fusilli
3	tbsp. unsalted butter
2	tbsp. olive oil
4	small zucchini, washed and sliced thinly
2	cloves garlic, peeled and mashed
4	medium tomatoes, peeled, seeded and chopped finely
2	cups cream
1	tsp. sea salt
1	tsp. freshly ground black pepper
12	basil leaves, torn into fragments
4	tbsp. soy parmesan cheese

1. Place butter and olive oil in large skillet. Turn heat to high. Add zucchini slices, tossing to insure golden color. Add garlic and toss. Add tomatoes, cream, salt and pepper. Cook over high heat 3-5 minutes until cream thickens. Remove from heat and stir in basil leaves.

2. Meanwhile, bring 4 quarts of water and 1 tbsp. of sea salt to boil in a large pan. Add pasta and cook according to package directions. Do not over cook. It should remain firm to the bite. Drain well.

3. Place pasta in shallow serving dish. Toss with sauce. Add cheese and toss gently. Serve.

Serves 4-6

PASTA WITH ALMOND AND GREEN TOMATO SAUCE

1	lb. whole wheat spaghetti
¾	cup olive oil
1	clove garlic, sliced thinly
¼	cup Italian parsley, finely chopped
1¾	lb. green tomatoes, cored and sliced thinly
1	tsp. sea salt
1	tsp. black pepper
4	tbsp. fresh almonds, sliced
1	tsp. freshly grated lemon peel
1	tbsp. unsalted butter
6	fresh basil leaves, torn in fragments

1. Combine olive oil, garlic and parsley in a large saute pan. Cook over low heat until garlic is tender but not browned. Add tomatoes, salt and pepper. Continue cooking until tomatoes begin to fall apart. Stir in almonds and lemon peel. Keep warm.

2. Meanwhile, bring 4 quarts of water and 1 tbsp. of sea salt to boil in a large pot. Add pasta and cook according to package directions. Do not over cook. It should be firm to the bite. Drain well.

3. Place pasta in shallow serving dish with butter and toss quickly. Add tomato sauce and toss gently. Sprinkle top with basil leaves and serve.

Serves 4-6

PASTA WITH GARBANZOS

1	lb. whole wheat penne or shells
2	15 oz. cans garbanzo beans <u>OR</u> 3 cups cooked garbanzos divided in half
1	tsp. fresh rosemary (2-3 inch sprig)
2	cloves garlic, peeled
1	tsp. sea salt
1	tsp. black pepper
⅔	cup extra virgin olive oil

1. Bring 4 quarts of water and 1 tbsp. of sea salt to boil in a large pot. Add pasta and cook according to directions on package. Do not over cook. It should remain firm to the bite. Drain, reserving cooking liquid.

2. Meanwhile, place half of garbanzo beans, rosemary, garlic, salt and pepper into food processor. Blend, adding olive oil slowly, until smooth paste is formed. Thin with cooking liquid from pasta so that sauce has the consistency of heavy cream.

3. Using a strainer, place remaining garbanzos into hot cooking liquid from pasta to warm. It need not be on the fire.

4. Place pasta in a shallow serving bowl. Toss with sauce. Gently stir remaining whole garbanzos. Serve immediately.

Serves 4-6

FETTUCCINE WITH PEAS AND MINT

1	lb. spinach fettuccine
1	small pinch of saffron (optional)
6	tbsp. unsalted butter
6	green onions, trimmed and sliced
1	tsp. sea salt
1	tsp. freshly ground black pepper
1½	lb. fresh peas, shelled or 2 cups frozen petite peas
3	tbsp. mint leaves, finely chopped
¼	cup soy parmesan (optional)

1. Soak saffron in a very small bowl with 2 tbsp. water.

2. Combine 4 tbsp. of butter, the onions, salt and pepper in a saute pan. Cook over low heat for 15 minutes or until onions are very tender but do not allow to brown. If using fresh peas, add peas and ½ cup water continue to cook over low heat until peas turn bright green. If using frozen peas, add to pan and cook on low until peas are warmed enough. Stir in mint and keep warm.

3. Meanwhile, bring 4 quarts of water and 1 tbsp. of sea salt to boil in a large pot. Add fettuccine and cook according to directions on package. Do not over cook. It should be firm to the bite.

4. Combine remaining butter with saffron water in a warmed serving bowl. Remove pasta from pot leaving water dripping from strands. Toss gently with saffron butter. Gently toss with sauce. Serve with soy parmesan.

Serves 4-6

PASTA WITH FENNEL AND TOMATOES

1	lb. whole wheat penne or other whole wheat tube pasta
1	fennel bulb, trimmed and sliced thinly
1	lb. tomatoes, peeled, seeded and chopped into fine dice
2	tbsp. sweet red onion, finely diced
1	clove garlic, peeled and mashed
½	cup extra virgin olive oil
2	tbsp. fresh lemon juice
1	tbsp. fresh mint, finely chopped
1	tbsp. fresh basil, finely chopped
½	tsp. sea salt
1	tsp. freshly ground pepper

1. Combine fennel, tomatoes, red onion, olive oil, lemon juice, mint, basil, salt and pepper in a large bowl.

2. Bring 4 quarts of water and 1 tbsp. sea salt to boil in a large pot. Add pasta and cook according to directions on package. Do not over cook. It should be firm to the bite. Drain well.

3. Toss hot pasta with raw vegetable mixture and serve immediately.

Serves 4- 6

PASTA WITH SPINACH AND POTATOES

1	lb. spinach fusilli pasta
½	lb. small red potatoes, quartered
½	cup virgin olive oil
½	cup yellow onion, roughly chopped
3	cloves garlic, freshly minced
3	bunches spinach, freshly washed
½	tsp. red pepper flakes
1	tsp. sea salt

1. Place potatoes in a pan of cold water. Bring to a boil and cook until just tender. Rinse under cool water to prevent over cooking.

2. Bring 4 quarts of water with 1 tbsp. sea salt to boil in a large pot and cook pasta according to the directions on the package. Do not over cook. It should be firm to the bite.

3. Meanwhile, heat oil in a large skillet. Add onions. Add garlic after onion has become soft and transparent. Add spinach. Continue to cook for 3-5 minutes until spinach is wilted. Add potatoes, red pepper flakes and sea salt if needed to correct seasoning. Cover pan.

4. Drain pasta, reserving ½ cup of cooking liquid. Toss pasta with spinach mixture. Add cooking liquid. Toss well and serve immediately.

Serves 4-6

PASTA WITH SWEET POTATOES

1	lb. durum fettucini
½	lb. sweet potatoes
¾	cup virgin olive oil
1	yellow onion, chopped
2	cloves garlic, minced
1	cup garbanzo beans
1	cup tomatoes, chopped (may be canned)
1	tsp. cinnamon
1	tsp. ginger
½	tsp. red pepper flakes
1	tsp. sea salt
1	tsp. black pepper

1. Cut sweet potatoes into pieces and boil until tender. Cut into smaller bite sized portions. Set aside.

2. Bring 4 quarts of water and 1 tbsp. sea salt to boil and cook pasta according to the directions on the package. Do not over cook. It should be firm to the bite.

3. Meanwhile, heat oil in large skillet. Add onions and saute until translucent. Add garlic, garbanzo beans and sweet potatoes. Add tomatoes, cinnamon, ginger, pepper flakes, salt and pepper. Cook over medium heat until flavors are blended and liquid from tomatoes is reduced.

3. Drain pasta. Toss with sauce and serve immediately.

Fusilli with Leeks and Endive

1 lb. whole wheat fusilli
1 large red pepper
⅓ cup extra virgin olive oil
1 clove garlic, peeled and mashed
4 medium leeks, cup in half lengthwise then sliced
1 cup Belgian endive, shredded finely lengthwise
1 tsp. black pepper
1 tsp. sea salt

1. Roast pepper until skin blisters. Place in a small bowl, then cover tightly with plastic wrap. Let sit 15 minutes. When cool, remove core, skin and seeds. Cut into narrow strips.

2. Place olive oil and garlic in skillet over medium heat. When garlic begins to color, add leeks and endive. Cover skillet, reduce heat to low. Allow vegetables to cook slowly, stirring occasionally for 20 minutes until they are very tender.

3. Meanwhile, bring 4 quarts of water and 1 tbsp. sea salt to boil in a large pot and cook pasta according to directions on the package. Do not over cook. It should be firm to the bite.

4. Add peppers to the leek mixture, then cook 2-3 minutes more.

5. Drain pasta, toss with sauce, add salt and pepper. Serve at once.

Makes 4-6 Servings

Pasta with Walnuts

1   lb. whole wheat spaghetti
¾   cup extra virgin olive oil
2   cloves garlic, peeled and mashed
2   cups walnut halves
1   tsp. sea salt
1   tsp. freshly ground pepper
1   cup Italian parsley, roughly chopped
1   tsp. fresh orange peel (optional)

1. Place olive oil and garlic in a large saute pan. Cook over low heat until garlic is translucent but not browned. Add walnuts, salt and pepper and cook for 2-3 minutes to lightly brown. Keep warm.

2. Meanwhile, bring 4 quarts of water and 1 tbsp. of sea salt to boil in a large pot. Cook pasta according to directions on package. Do not over cook. Pasta should remain firm to the bite. Drain, reserving ½ cup of cooking liquid.

3. Place pasta in a shallow serving bowl. Toss with nut mixture, parsley, orange peel and reserved cooking liquid. Serve.

Serves 4-6

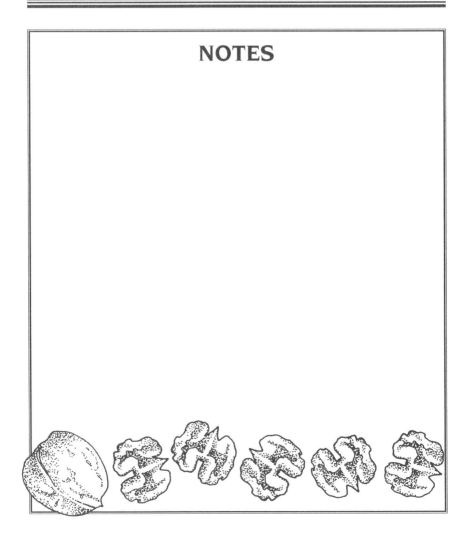

NOTES

EGGPLANT PASTA

1   lb. whole wheat pasta shells
2   small eggplants, sliced into rounds
½   cup olive oil
2   cloves garlic, peeled and mashed
1   lb. fresh plum tomatoes, peeled, seeded and coarsely chopped or 1- 28 oz. can Italian plum tomatoes, seeded, chopped and drained
½   tsp. dried red pepper flakes
½   tsp. black pepper
1   tbsp. fresh basil, chopped
1   tbsp. fresh parsley, chopped
1   tsp. salt
½   cup soy parmesan

1. Place sliced eggplant in colander and sprinkle with ½ tsp. of salt. Let drain for 30 minutes. Rinse well to remove salt and dry with a paper towel.

2. Place ¼ cup of olive oil and garlic in large skillet. Cook for 2-3 minutes until garlic begins to color. Add chopped tomatoes, pepper flakes, pepper, basil, parsley and remaining salt. Cook for 15 minutes until sauce thickens. Set aside and keep warm.

3. Bring 4 quarts of water and 1 tbsp. sea salt to boil in large pot. Add past and cook according to package directions. Do not over cook. It should be firm to the bite. Drain.

4. While pasta cooks, saute eggplant slices in remaining olive oil 3-5 minutes per side to brown evenly. Place on warm plates.

5. Gently toss cooked pasta with tomato sauce. Serve pasta over eggplant slices. Sprinkle with cheese.

Serves 4-6

PASTA WITH CAULIFLOWER AND SUN DRIED TOMATOES

1   lb. small whole wheat pasta shells
1   head cauliflower
½   cup extra virgin olive oil
1   large onion, diced
4   tbsp. sun dried tomato paste or imported Italian
    tomato paste
4   tbsp. raisins
4   tbsp. pine nuts
1   tsp. sea salt
1   tsp. black pepper

1. Cook cauliflower 12-14 minutes in abundant boiling water until tender but still crisp. Lift cauliflower from water, reserving the liquid. Cut away stalk and outer leaves, then cut into small flowerets.

2. In large heavy bottomed sauce pan, or braising pan, combine oil and onion. Cook over low heat for 5 minutes. Add 3 tbsp. of reserved cooking liquid. Continue cooking until onion is very translucent and tender. Add tomato paste and 1 cup of reserved liquid. Bring to a gentle simmer, cover and cook for 10 minutes.

3. Add cauliflower, raisins, pine nuts, salt and pepper. Cook, covered, over low heat for 30 minutes stirring occasionally. Use a fork to break up cauliflower pieces. Add up to 1 cup reserved liquid as needed until cauliflower forms a coarse puree. Season with salt and pepper.

4. Meanwhile, bring 4 quarts of water and 1 tbsp. of sea salt to boil in a large pot. Add pasta and cook according to directions on package. Do not over cook. It should remain firm to the bite. Drain.

5. Place pasta in shallow serving bowl. Drizzle with 1 tbsp. of olive oil and toss. Add sauce and toss. Let pasta rest for 1 minute. Toss again. Serve.

Serves 4-6

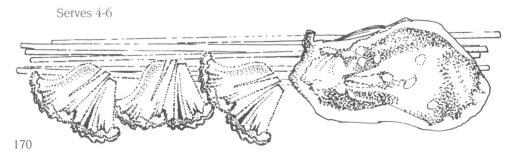

PASTA WITH POTATOES AND TOMATOES

1	lb. whole wheat spaghetti
1	cup fresh basil leaves, stems removed
3	cloves garlic, peeled
2	tbsp. pine nuts
6	tbsp. olive oil
4	large ripe tomatoes, peeled and chopped
½	tsp. dried red pepper flakes
1	tsp. sea salt
2	medium potatoes, boiled and cut into ¼" dice
4	tbsp. soy "parmesan" cheese

1. Combine basil, garlic, pine nuts and 4 tbsp. of olive oil in a food processor or blender. Process until a rough paste is formed.

2. Place tomatoes, pesto, salt and pepper flakes in a small bowl. Mash together with a fork. Set aside.

3. Bring 4 quarts of water and 1 tbsp. sea salt to boil in a large pot. Add pasta and cook according to directions on package. Do not over cook. It should be firm to the bite. Drain, reserving ¼ cup of cooking liquid.

4. Meanwhile, toss potatoes with remaining 2 tbsp. of olive oil. Place under preheated broiler until potatoes are golden and crusty. Drain on paper towel.

5. Place pasta in a shallow serving dish. Add raw tomatoes and potatoes. Toss well. Add a little of cooking liquid to help tomato sauce spread evenly though the pasta. Sprinkle with parmesan and serve

Serves 4-6

VEGETABLES

VEGETABLES

ROOTS, SEEDS, LEAVES AND STEMS

It's been said a million times in a million ways, and it's still true: *raw is best*. Only in its raw state does a vegetable have every iota of nourishment nature intended. As soon as its natural state is altered, the beloved veggie starts to lose its nutritional power.

You'll find many excellent recipes for raw vegetables in the *Salads* section of this book. But if you are going to eat *cooked* vegetables, the healthiest way will always be lightly steamed until just tender, possibly served with a little lemon juice, sea salt and pepper. However, both our lifestyles and our palates often demand more than just another meal served with lightly steamed vegetables. Vegetable cookery, at its finest, offers a variety of methods and techniques that can bring even unfamiliar or previously disliked vegetables to an imaginative and tasty finale.

Under ideal conditions, all your vegetables will come from your own or your neighbor's garden, but often this just isn't possible. So you may have to pay a little more for fresh, organic vegetables that are available all year round at your farmer's market, health food store or specialty store. When it comes to vegetables, the requirement of freshness cannot be overstated. It may help to remember that the Livingston diet doesn't require you to spend your food budget on high-cost meat products, so don't panic if the freshest vegetables seem a bit pricey -- it's worth every cent!

Green leaf vegetables are rich sources of vitamin A and C. Abscisic Acid, an analog of the A group, is found in most root vegetables and a variety of other vegetables. Kale, peas and beans include some of the B vitamins as well. Most vegetables also include some of the amino acids our bodies require for growth and cell repair. While no vegetable contains all the essential acids, most of these recipes combine several vegetables in certain combinations, such as green beans and corn, to provide the complete complement of amino acids. Overall, a diet in which calories are based on vegetables and grains certainly provides sufficient protein for any individual.

Just as with the grains and legumes, experiment with these recipes, then create your own. Remember, the only guidelines are: buy the freshest vegetables you can find, and *never, never* overcook them.

SPRING GREENS

8   cups greens, such as turnip, beet, chard, spinach or a mixture which could include watercress and dandelion as well

2   tbsp. flaxseed or safflower oil

1   large onion, sliced thinly

1½   tbsp. molasses

3   tbsp. apple cider vinegar

1. Place washed greens in a steamer. Steam until just wilted. Chop greens coarsely with a knife.

2. Heat oil in skillet over medium heat. Add onions, cooking until translucent but not brown. Meanwhile, mix molasses and vinegar together in a small bowl. Add to onion mixture, stirring well. Add greens. Toss to mix well and serve.

Serves 4

SPINACH WITH CURRANTS AND NUTS

6   bunches spinach, washed and stems removed

¼   cup olive oil

½   cup pine nuts

⅔   cup currants, soaked in warm water for 30 minutes and well drained

½   tsp. sea salt

½   tsp. black pepper

1. Place spinach in a steamer. Steam until just wilted. Squeeze out extra moisture.

2. Heat oil over medium heat in a fireproof casserole or heavy skillet. Add pine nuts. Cook over medium heat until they begin to color. Add currants and stir well. Add spinach, salt and pepper. Heat through. Serve immediately.

Serves 4-6

LEMON BROCCOLI WITH ALMONDS

2	bunches broccoli
4	tbsp. butter
⅓	cup almonds, slivered
1	clove garlic, chopped finely
1	tsp. sea salt
1	tsp. black pepper
1	lemon, juiced and rind grated

1. Cut broccoli into medium sliced flowerets with about 2-3 inches of stem attached. Place broccoli in steamer. Steam until broccoli has become bright green and is tender-crisp to the bite. Depending on the size of your steamer this could take from 7-12 minutes.

2. Meanwhile, heat butter over low heat in a large skillet. Add almonds, cooking until just golden. Add garlic, salt, pepper and lemon juice. Keep warm.

3. When broccoli is cooked, transfer to shallow serving dish. Toss with almond sauce. Garnish with reserved lemon peel.

Serves 4-6

STIR FRIED BROCCOLI

2	bunches broccoli
2	tbsp. flaxseed or safflower oil
1	tsp. sea salt
2	tbsp. water
1	tsp. honey
1	tsp. cornstarch mixed with 2 tbsp. cold water

1. Separate small florets from the large stems. Cut large stems thinly on diagonal.

2. In a wok, or other large skillet, heat oil over high heat. Add broccoli and stir fry for 2 minutes. Add salt, water and honey. Toss well. Cover and continue cooking for 2 minutes longer, stirring once. Add corn starch mixture. Toss well. Cook 1 minute more. Serve immediately.

Serves 4-6

CABBAGE ROLLS WITH MUSHROOMS

STUFFING

2	medium potatoes, peeled
¼	cup cream
4	tbsp. butter
¼	lb. mushrooms, brushed and finely chopped
⅓	cup almonds, slivered
2	tbsp. chives, finely cut
1	tbsp. parsley, finely chopped
1	tbsp. pomegranate seeds or small capers, rinsed and drained
1	tsp. sea salt
1	tsp. black pepper
6	large cabbage leaves, blanched in boiling water for 1 minute and drained
2	tbsp. butter
½	tsp. vegesal
¼	tsp. turmeric
2-3	tbsp. water

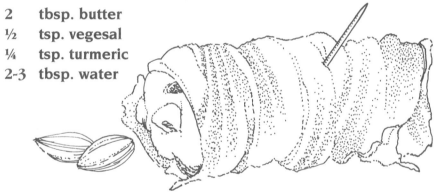

1. To make stuffing, boil potatoes until tender. Drain, then mash with cream and butter. Add mushrooms, almonds, chives, parsley, pomegranate seeds or capers, salt and pepper. Mix well.

2. Blanch cabbage leaves in boiling water for 1 minute. Drain.

3. Place one sixth of mixture in the middle of each cabbage leaf. Wrap up leaves and secure with wooden toothpick or tie with string.

4. Heat butter in large skillet over high heat. Add cabbage rolls, turning frequently until the leaves have browned on all sides. Sprinkle turmeric and vegesal over cabbage rolls. Add water. Reduce heat, cover and steam until moisture has evaporated. Uncover and continue cooking for 2-3 minutes to evaporate liquid.

Serves 6

MIDEASTERN STUFFED CABBAGE

STUFFING

½   cup kashi, cooked
½   cup brown rice, cooked
½   medium onion, chopped finely
¼   lb. mushrooms, finely chopped
¼   cup fresh pineapple, chopped
¼   cup dried figs, chopped
2   tbsp. currants
2   tbsp. pecans, toasted and chopped
½   tsp. curry powder
½   tsp. ground ginger
½   tsp. savory
1   tsp. sea salt

6   large cabbage leaves
1   tbsp. olive oil
¼   cup drinking water

1. In a large mixing bowl, combine all stuffing ingredients. Toss well.

2. Blanch cabbage leaves in boiling water for 1 minute. Drain.

3. Pour olive oil into 8x8 glass baking dish. Place one sixth of mixture in the middle of each cabbage leaf. Fold sides over then roll from stem end. Place in rolled-side down in baking dish. Continue until all have been rolled and fit together neatly in dish. Pour water over top. Cover and bake at 325° for 30 minutes until cabbage is tender when pierced with a fork. Remove cover and continue baking for 5 minutes to evaporate excess liquid.

Serves 6

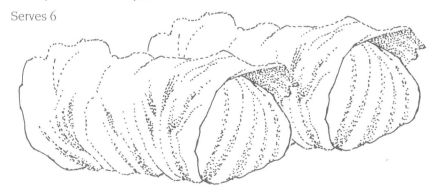

GINGERED GREEN BEANS

1	lb. green beans, strings removed
1	tbsp. butter
1	small onion, sliced thinly
2	tsp. fresh ginger
½	tsp. sea salt
¼	tsp. ground fennel seed

1. Slice beans slantwise into 1 inch slivers. In a large sauce pan, bring to boil 2 tbsp. of water with butter. Add beans, onion, ginger, salt and fennel seed. Cover tightly and let beans steam for 5-7 minutes. Do not overcook beans. Serve very hot.

Serves 2-4

GREEN BEANS WITH GARLIC

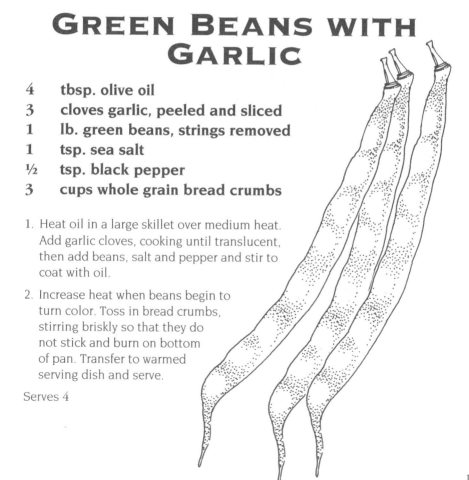

4	tbsp. olive oil
3	cloves garlic, peeled and sliced
1	lb. green beans, strings removed
1	tsp. sea salt
½	tsp. black pepper
3	cups whole grain bread crumbs

1. Heat oil in a large skillet over medium heat. Add garlic cloves, cooking until translucent, then add beans, salt and pepper and stir to coat with oil.

2. Increase heat when beans begin to turn color. Toss in bread crumbs, stirring briskly so that they do not stick and burn on bottom of pan. Transfer to warmed serving dish and serve.

Serves 4

POLISH BEETS

2   tbsp. butter
4   cups beets, coarsely grated
1   tbsp. butter
3   tbsp. lemon juice
1½   tsp. salt
½   tsp. pepper
1   tbsp. whole wheat flour
½   cup water

1. In a large skillet, heat butter over medium heat. Add beets, lemon juice, salt and pepper. Cover and cook for 25 minutes over very low heat.
2. Sprinkle flour over top of beets. Do not stir. Cover the skillet again and continue cooking for 15 minutes, then stir and add water. Bring to a boil and serve.

Serves 6

JERUSALEM ARTICHOKES DAUBE

2   tbsp. olive oil
1   medium onion, chopped finely
1½   lb. Jerusalem artichokes, scrubbed and diced coarsely
2   cloves garlic, chopped finely
½   tsp. sea salt
½   tsp. black pepper
1   bouquet garni
¼   tsp. nutmeg
½   cup vegetable stock
½   cup drinking water

1. In a fireproof earthen or enamel casserole, heat oil over medium heat. Add onion and cook until translucent but not browned. Add artichokes, garlic, salt, pepper and bouquet garni. Cover and allow to simmer for 15 minutes shaking casserole occasionally.

2. Pour vegetable stock and water over artichokes. Cook over high heat 3-5 minutes until almost all liquid has evaporated. Reduce heat to very low and continue cooking for 1 hour.

Serves 4

JERUSALEM ARTICHOKES AU GRATIN

6	**Jerusalem artichokes, scrubbed**
6	**tbsp. butter**
¼	**cup whole grain bread crumbs**
4	**tbsp. whole wheat pastry flour**
¾	**cup cream**
¾	**cup vegetable stock**

1. Steam artichokes until tender. Cool just until you can handle them, then cut into cubes. Place in a covered casserole and keep warm.

2. In a medium sauce pan, melt butter. Drizzle 2 tbsp. of melted butter over bread crumbs to moisten. Set aside.

3. Add flour to remaining butter. Cook for 2 minutes over low heat, stirring constantly with a wooden spoon. Slowly add cream and stock, beating constantly to prevent any lumps from forming. Pour sauce over artichokes. Top with bread crumbs. Bake at 300° for 30 minutes or until artichokes are easily pierced with a fork, sauce is bubbly and bread crumbs have browned.

Serves 4-6

NOTES

CRUSTY HERBED CAULIFLOWER

1	large cauliflower
1	tbsp. egg replacer mixed with 4 tbsp. water or 2 San Pasqual eggs, beaten
½	tsp. sea salt
1	cup whole grain bread crumbs
¼	cup basil, chopped
¼	cup parsley, chopped
3	tbsp. whole wheat flour
1	tsp. spike
2	tbsp. melted butter

1. Cut cauliflower into florets. Place in steamer and steam 10-12 minutes until just tender.

2. Meanwhile, mix together egg replacer and salt in a small bowl. In a separate bowl, mix together bread crumbs, basil and parsley.

3. Toss florets with flour and spike to dust lightly. Dip each into egg replacer mixture, then bread crumb mixture. Place on non-stick or oiled baking sheet. Drizzle with melted butter. Bake in preheated 350° oven for 20-25 minutes until golden and crispy.

Serves 6

CAULIFLOWER BENARASI

1	large cauliflower, cut into small florets
½	tsp. cumin seeds
¼	tsp. caraway seeds
¼	tsp. black pepper corns
2	whole cloves
1	whole bay leaf
1½	onion, chopped
1½	cup canned tomato with 1/2 cup of liquid reserved
2	tsp. coriander, ground
¼	tsp. turmeric

½	tsp. cayenne
¼	tsp. cardamon
1	tsp. sea salt
5	tbsp. butter

1. Place cauliflower in steamer and steam for 10 minutes until just barely tender. Set aside.

2. With mortar and pestle, or in blender, pulverize cumin, caraway, peppercorns, cloves and bay leaf. Set aside.

3. Place onions, tomatoes and their reserved cooking liquid, coriander, turmeric, cayenne, cardomon and salt in blender. Puree until smooth. In medium sauce pan, heat butter over medium heat. Add tomato mixture, cook partially covered for 10 minutes, until thickened. Stir frequently to prevent sticking. Add pulverized spices to sauce.

4. Toss sauce with cauliflower florets. Place in a baking dish, cover and bake for 30 minutes until tender. Serve immediately.

Serves 4-6

NOTES

CALABACITAS

2	tbsp. flaxseed or safflower oil
1	small onion, chopped
1	tsp. sea salt
½	tsp. black pepper
4	ears fresh corn, cut from cob OR 1-10oz. package frozen corn
3	medium tomatoes, seeded and chopped
2	tbsp. Ortega chilies, diced
3	medium zucchini, sliced
1	cup soy jack cheese

1. In flameproof casserole, or large deep skillet, heat oil over medium heat. Add onions, salt and pepper. Cook until translucent but not browned. Add corn, tomatoes and chilies. Cover and steam for 5-7 minutes. Add zucchini. Cover and steam 5 minutes more. Top with cheese, replace cover and continue cooking just until cheese melts. Serve immediately.

Serves 6

JAPANESE SNOW PEAS

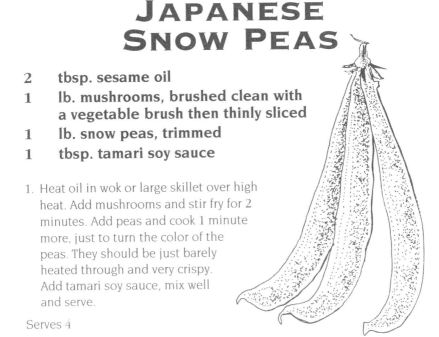

2	tbsp. sesame oil
1	lb. mushrooms, brushed clean with a vegetable brush then thinly sliced
1	lb. snow peas, trimmed
1	tbsp. tamari soy sauce

1. Heat oil in wok or large skillet over high heat. Add mushrooms and stir fry for 2 minutes. Add peas and cook 1 minute more, just to turn the color of the peas. They should be just barely heated through and very crispy. Add tamari soy sauce, mix well and serve.

Serves 4

New Potatoes Duxelle

1½ lb. small new potatoes
2   tbsp. butter
3   scallions, finely chopped including green tops
1½ lb. mushrooms, brushed clean with a vegetable brush and finely chopped
2   tbsp. whole wheat pastry flour
1½ cup vegetable broth
1   bay leaf
1   tsp. sea salt
1   tsp. black pepper
2   tsp. parsley, finely chopped

1. Place potatoes in a steamer. Steam for 15 minutes. Set aside.

2. Meanwhile, melt butter in a heavy sauce pan over medium heat. Add scallions, cooking for 2-3 minutes. Add mushrooms and continue cooking for 3-4 minutes. Stir in flour. Mix well until thoroughly incorporated. Gradually add broth, stirring all the time to keep sauce smooth. Add bay leaf, salt and pepper. Bring to a boil, then reduce heat and simmer for 8 minutes. Remove bay leaf.

3. Add potatoes to sauce, stirring gently to coat potatoes. Heat through. Place in a shallow serving dish and garnish with parsley.

Serves 4-6

Mashed Potatoes with Turnips

1   lb. medium sized potatoes
1   lb. young turnips
6   tbsp. butter
1/3 cup cream
1   tsp. sea salt
1   tsp. black pepper

1. Place potatoes in a pot of boiling water. Boil 20 minutes or until tender. Meanwhile, steam turnips for 15-20 minutes until tender.
2. Using a potato masher, or hand beater, whip potatoes and turnips together with butter, cream, salt and pepper. Heat through and serve.

Serves 4

BAKED POTATOES WITH LEEKS

4	large baking potatoes
4	tbsp. butter
2	leeks, split, washed and finely sliced
1	tsp. sea salt
1	tsp. black pepper
⅓	cup cream
1	tbsp. any fresh herb, finely chopped
2	tbsp. soy parmesan cheese

1. Bake potatoes in a 400° oven for 50 minutes or until soft when pierced with a fork. Allow to cool enough to handle. Split potatoes in half lengthwise.

2. Meanwhile, heat butter in a medium skillet. Add leeks and cook over low heat until leeks are very soft and translucent. Season with salt and pepper.

3. Scoop out the pulp of the potatoes, careful not to break the shells. Place pulp in mixing bowl, breaking it up with a fork or whisk. Add cream and beat until smooth. Fold in leek mixture and fresh herbs. Refill potato skins, sprinkle tops with cheese and put under broiler for 5 minutes or until browned.

Serves 4

NOTES

LANGUEDOC POTATOES

3	tbsp. olive oil
2	large tomatoes, seeded and chopped
1	tbsp. butter
¼	cup onion, chopped
1	clove garlic, peeled and mashed
2	lb. large baking potatoes, sliced thickly
1	tsp. sea salt
1	tsp. pepper
1	tsp. dried thyme
1	bay leaf, crumbled
1	cup vegetable stock

1. In a small skillet, heat 2 tbsp. of olive oil over medium heat. Add tomatoes and cook for 5 minutes.

2. In a fireproof casserole, heat 1 tbsp. olive oil and butter. Add onions and garlic. Cook over medium heat until translucent but not browned. Layer potatoes on top. Cover with tomato sauce. Season with salt, pepper, thyme and bay leaf. Pour stock over tomatoes. Cover and bake in a 325° oven for 1 hour.

Serves 4

STUFFED SWEET POTATOES

6	medium sweet potatoes or yams
½	cup cream
3	tbsp. orange juice
1	tsp. fresh orange peel, grated
3	tbsp. butter
1	tsp. sea salt

1. Bake sweet potatoes or yams in 400° oven for 50 minutes until easily pierced with a fork. Scoop out flesh.

2. Using a fork or potato mash, whip pulp with cream, orange juice, peel, butter and salt until smooth. Return to oven for 5 minutes to heat through.

Serves 6

Baked Sweet Potatoes with Caramelized Apples

3   large sweet potatoes
4   tbsp. butter
3   large apples, cored and sliced
1   tsp. salt
¼   cup raw honey mixed with ¼ cup of hot water

1. Place sweet potatoes in steamer. Steam for 20 minutes until tender when pierced with a fork. Peel, slice and set aside.

2. Meanwhile, heat 3 tbsp. of butter in a large skillet. Add apple slices and cook until light brown.

3. Arrange sweet potatoes and apples in alternate layers in a buttered 1½ quart baking dish. Sprinkle with salt. Drizzle honey over the top, then dot with remaining butter pieces. Bake in a preheated 350° oven for 30 minutes until honey has been absorbed and the top is lightly browned.

Serves 6

Eggplant Puree

2½   lb. eggplant, peeled and cubed
¼   cup olive oil
2   cloves garlic, peeled and mashed
1   tsp. paprika
½   tsp. sea salt
½   tsp. black pepper

1. Steam eggplant for 20 minutes until soft. Allow to drain.

2. Heat oil over medium heat in a large skillet. Add eggplant, garlic, paprika, salt and pepper. Allow to cook, stirring constantly for 10 minutes until eggplant becomes a smooth puree. Serve hot.

Serves 4

EGGPLANT CASSEROLE

1	lb. eggplant, peeled and cubed (2 cups)
2	cups whole grain bread crumbs
1	medium onion, chopped
2	cloves garlic, peeled and mashed
½	cup green bell pepper, diced
1	cup tomato sauce
1	tbsp. fresh basil, chopped or 1/2 tsp. dried
½	tsp. oregano
½	tsp. thyme
½	tsp. nutmeg
1	tsp. sea salt
1	cup soy jack cheese, grated

1. In a large bowl, combine all ingredients except soy cheese. Place in oiled casserole and bake at 350° for 45 minutes. Sprinkle cheese over top. Bake 15 minutes more.

Serves 4-6

BAKED TOMATOES

8	medium tomatoes
4	cloves garlic, peeled and slivered
1½	cups whole wheat sourdough bread crumbs
2	tbsp. fresh parsley, chopped
½	cup olive oil

1. Remove hard core from tomatoes with tip of knife. Slice off tops. Push garlic slivers down into sections of each tomato and place in shallow baking dish.

2. Mix crumbs with parsley, salt and pepper. Lightly stuff centers of tomatoes, piling bread crumbs on top of each. Drizzle with oil. Bake in preheated 400° oven for 20-25 minutes until tops are golden and tomatoes are soft. Serve warm or break on top of a nest of freshly cooked pasta.

Serves 4

SWEET PEPPERS WITH TOMATOES

½   cup extra virgin olive oil
1   large onion, diced
2   cloves garlic, thinly sliced
6   small bay leaves
6   red, green or yellow bell peppers or a mix of any
     or all, seeded and cut into long strips
1   tsp. sea salt
1   tsp. black pepper
4   medium tomatoes, seeded and cut into long strips
1   tbsp. lemon juice

1. Heat oil in a large skillet over medium heat. Add onion, garlic and bay leaves. Cook until onion is translucent but not browned. Add peppers, salt and pepper. Continue cooking for 10 minutes, stirring frequently.

2. Remove bay leaves. Add tomatoes and cook for another 10 minutes. Stir in lemon juice. Serve warm or at room temperature.

Serves4- 6

BAKED BUTTERNUT SQUASH

1   large butternut squash
2   tsp. anise seed, crushed
⅛   tsp. ground cardamom
½   tsp. sea salt
½   tsp. pepper
3   tbsp. raw honey
2   tbsp. lemon juice
4   tbsp. butter, melted

1. Cut and peel squash. Remove fibers and cut into 1 inch cubes. Place in buttered 2 quart baking dish. Sprinkle with anise, cardamom, salt and pepper. Drizzle with honey, lemon juice and butter. Bake uncovered in preheated 350° oven until tender.

Serves 4

STEAMED CHAYOTE AND CHEESE

3   chayotes, peeled and cubed
2   tbsp. butter
1   tsp. chili powder
½   tsp. sea salt
1   cup soy jack cheese, grated

1. Steam chayote in steamer 10-12 minutes until tender. Drain. Melt butter in drained steamer. Add chayotes, chili powder and salt. Stir gently. Top with cheese. Cover tightly and continue cooking over low heat just until cheese melts.

Serves 4

PUMPKIN WITH TOMATOES

2   lb. pumpkin meat, cut into pieces ½ inch wide and 3 inches long
⅓   cup olive oil
3   medium tomatoes, sliced crosswise
2   cloves garlic
2   tbsp. fresh parsley
1   tsp. sea salt
½   tsp. pepper
¼   cup whole grain bread crumbs
2   tbsp. butter

1. Blanch pumpkin in boiling water for 5 minutes. Remove and dry with paper toweling. Heat 3 tbsp. of oil in a large skillet. Add pumpkin and cook over medium heat until pieces begin to look translucent. Transfer to oven proof dish.

2. Add rest of oil to skillet. Add tomatoes, garlic, 1 tbsp. of parsley, salt and pepper. Cook, stirring frequently, over medium heat until tomatoes disintegrate and liquid has reduced by half.

3. Spread tomato mixture over pumpkin. Mix remaining parsley with bread crumbs. Sprinkle over top, then dot with butter. Bake in preheated oven at 400° for 20 minutes.

Serves 4-6

Zucchini
with Walnuts

3   tbsp. butter
8   small zucchini, trimmed and sliced into 1/2" slices
¼   cup walnuts, coarsely chopped
2   tsp. fresh sage leaves, coarsely chopped
½   tsp. sea salt
½   tsp. black pepper

1. Heat 2 tbsp. of butter in large skillet over medium heat. Add zucchini. Cook 3-5 minutes, just until zucchini begins to soften.

2. Meanwhile, heat remaining butter in medium skillet. Add walnuts and sage, then cook, stirring constantly until just browned.

3. Combine walnut mixture with zucchini. Add salt and pepper. Toss well, then continue cooking 3-5 minutes until zucchini is tender.

Serves 4

Summer Squash
with Piquant Sauce

3   tbsp. olive oil
2   cloves garlic
1½   lb. summer squash, scrubbed and sliced thinly
½   tsp. sea salt
½   tsp. black pepper
1   tbsp. red wine vinegar
¼   cup fresh basil, coarsely chopped

1. Heat olive oil in deep skillet over medium heat. Add garlic, cooking until just golden. Discard garlic.

2. Add squash, salt and pepper. Cook squash over medium heat, stirring frequently 3-5 minutes until tender but still crisp. Stir in vinegar and basil. Cook 1 minute more.

Serves 4-6

STIR FRY ASPARAGUS

2   lb. asparagus, tough end trimmed off
2   tbsp. safflower oil
3   tbsp. soy sauce
1   tbsp. lemon juice
½   tsp. sea salt
½   tsp. black pepper

1. Cut asparagus into thin diagonal slices. Place in steamer and steam just until asparagus turns bright green. Remove from steamer basket at once.

2. Heat oil in wok or large skillet. Add asparagus, soy sauce, lemon juice, salt and pepper. Toss well to coat. Cook for 1 minute. Do not over cook. Serve.

Serves 4

ASPARAGUS WITH ASPARAGUS SAUCE

2   lb. asparagus, rough ends trimmed
4   tbsp. butter
1   tsp. sea salt
½   tsp. black pepper
½   cup reserved cooking liquid

1. Peel asparagus stalks. Place peelings in small sauce pan with 1½ cups water. Bring to boil and cook over medium heat until tender but still bright green. Place butter, peelings, salt and pepper in food processor. Process, adding reserved cooking liquid from peelings until sauce has same consistency as cream. Keep warm.

2. Meanwhile, steam asparagus spears in steamer until just barely tender but still crisp. Place asparagus on warmed serving platter. Pour sauce over top and serve.

Serves 4

GRAINS &
LEGUMES

GRAINS AND LEGUMES
BEANS, RICE, LENTILS AND MORE

The primary source of protein in the Livingston Foundation diet is grains and legumes, since dairy products, with the exception of cream and butter, are disallowed.

Dried beans, lentils, peas, and their relatives are actually seeds because they come from the seed-pods of leguminous plants. They have been cultivated for centuries because early agricultural man discovered that when legumes are dried, they retain their nutritional value. Moreover, when they are rehydrated, they multiply their bulk to satisfy the appetite while providing nutrients to the body. Their average protein content is about 22% by weight, except for the highly revered soybean, known as the "cow of the East", which is 40% protein.

For complicated chemical reasons, any legume by itself is incomplete as a protein source, hence must be complemented with a grain. This doesn't mean you have to mix them together in the same bowl, but merely that they should be eaten at the same meal. When boiling dried legumes, use purified drinking water, as contaminents from "tap water" sources may detract from the healthfulness of the rehydrated product.

Tofu and tempeh may be added to any recipe to increase the protein content. These ingredients are usually found in oriental recipes, but it is a good idea to experiment with them in other cuisines as well. They make a delicious addition to any recipe. Tempeh is especially tasty, and blends well in a great variety of foods. If you prefer a chewier texture, freeze tofu before cutting it up to add to various dishes.

Like legumes, grains have been a mainstay of human sustenance throughout history. Grains are the seeds of grasses which are either grown in the wild or cultivated commercially. The seeds are collected as the grasses ripen, insuring that the protein content is captured in the drying process.

Serving grain and legume dishes can be a delectable culinary adventure. We encourage your own experimentation with grains and legumes in your favorite dishes as well as those offered here. We're certain that by mixing and matching you will find that you can create meals that are both satisfying to the palate and nutritionally sound.

So, like the Egyptians, Chinese, Etruscans, Aztecs and all the other harvesting cultures before us, build your culinary base from the most well-loved staples the earth has to offer; grains and legumes!

GREEK BAKED BEANS

2   cups dried Great Northern or Navy beans, soaked overnight and drained
10   cups drinking water
¼   cup olive oil
2   onions, chopped
1   cup tomato puree
3   tbsp. raw honey
2   tbsp. red wine vinegar
1   clove garlic
1   bay leaf
2   whole cloves
¼   cup soy parmesan

1. Place beans in a large stock pot, cover with drinking water and cook for 2 hours until tender. Add water if necessary. Drain.

2. Heat olive oil in sauce pan. Add onions and cook over medium heat until onions are translucent but not browned. Add tomato puree, honey, vinegar, garlic, bay leaf and cloves plus 2 cups of drinking water. Bring to a boil to make sauce.

3. In a shallow baking dish, mix beans with sauce. Bake for 30 minutes in a preheated 375° oven. Sprinkle with cheese, return to oven for 5 minutes and serve.

Serves 4-6

BEAN POLENTA

2   cups dried red or navy beans, soaked overnight and drained
3   tbsp. fresh lemon juice
1   tbsp. molasses
1   tbsp. red wine vinegar
1   tbsp. butter
1½ tsp. prepared mustard
2   tsp. sea salt
1   tsp. black pepper
     drinking water for beans

1. Place beans in a pot, cover them with cold drinking water. Bring water to a boil, then simmer, adding just enough water to keep beans covered for two hours.

2. Pour beans into a sieve and press them through. Place resulting pulp in a large skillet with lemon juice, molasses, vinegar, butter, mustard, salt and pepper. Gently heat for 5-7 minutes. Serve.

Serves 4- 6

CHINESE ADZUKI BEANS

2	**cups dried adzuki beans**
3	**cups drinking water**
1	**clove garlic, peeled**
6	**peppercorns**
1	**1 inch piece of fresh ginger, peeled**
1	**1 inch cinnamon stick**
10	**coriander seeds**
2	**whole cloves**
1	**onion, peeled but left whole**
1	**tsp. sea salt**
¼	**cup molasses**
1	**tbsp. tamari soy sauce**
1	**tbsp. sweet sherry (optional)**

1. In a soup pot, place 1 cup of adzuki beans with water. Bring to boil.

2. Meanwhile, place garlic, peppercorns, ginger, cinnamon, coriander seeds and cloves in a square of doubled cheesecloth. Tie together to form a spice bag.

3. Place spice bag, onion, salt and remaining adzuki beans into the pot. Bring mixture to boil again, then cover and simmer over low heat for two hours until beans are tender.

4. Remove whole onion and spice bag. Stir in molasses, tamari and sherry, if using.

Serves 4

BAKED BLACK BEANS

2	cups dried black beans
1	large onion, sliced
2	ribs celery with leaves, whole
1	clove garlic, peeled
1	bay leaf
6	parsley sprigs
2	tsp. sea salt
1	tsp. cumin
1	tsp. black pepper
½	tsp. cayenne pepper
2	tbsp. dark rum (optional)
3	limes, cut into quarters
2	tbsp. fresh cilantro, chopped
½	cup cream, soured with 1 tbsp. lemon juice
	drinking water

1. Place beans, onion, celery, garlic, bay leaf and parsley in a large stock pot. Cover with drinking water to cover. Bring mixture to boil, then reduce heat and simmer for 1 hour. Remove garlic, celery, bay leaf and parsley.

2. Add sea salt, cumin, black pepper, cayenne, rum and two of the quartered limes. Place beans in oven proof casserole in a 300° oven. Add additional water if needed just to barely cover beans. Bake beans for 1 hour, stirring occasionally.

3. Serve beans with the additional lime wedges, cilantro and soured cream as toppings

Serves 4-6

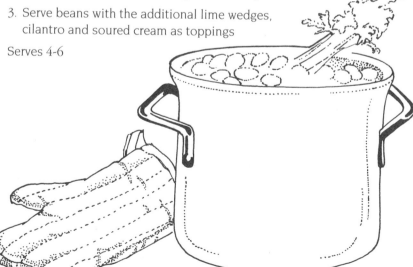

FLAGEOLETS

2   cups dried flageolets beans, soaked over night in 3 cups of drinking water

1   tsp. sea salt

2   tbsp. olive oil

1   clove garlic, peeled and mashed

3   medium tomatoes, peeled and quartered

1. Place beans in a pot with their soaking liquid and sea salt. Bring to boil. Reduce heat, cover and simmer for 1½-2 hours until soft. Drain beans.

2. Heat olive oil in a heavy, deep pan. Add garlic, cooking for 2-3 minutes over low heat to flavor oil. Add tomatoes and cooked flageolets. Allow to simmer for 20 minutes more on low heat to blend flavors. Adjust seasoning.

Serves 4

SAFFRON BEANS

2   cups dried, Great Northern or navy beans, soaked overnight and drained

4   onions, 2 chopped and 2 sliced thinly

8   tbsp. butter

¼   tsp. powdered saffron, steeped in 2 tbsp. of warm water

2   tsp. sea salt

2   tsp. black pepper

6   tbsp. parsley, chopped finely

1. Place beans in heavy bottomed, stove top casserole with chopped onions, butter and saffron. Add enough water to cover by 1 inch. Place lid on casserole and simmer for 2 hours until beans are tender.

2. Add sliced onions, salt, pepper and parsley. Continue cooking for 15 minutes until onion slices are soft. Thin with water if sauce is too thick.

Serves 4-6

KIDNEY BEANS WITH WALNUT SAUCE

1	cup dried kidney beans, soaked overnight and drained <u>OR</u> 2cups canned kidney beans heated (begin recipe at step 2)
2	tsp. sea salt
⅓	cup walnut pieces
1	clove garlic, peeled and mashed
¼	tsp. cayenne pepper
1	tbsp. red wine vinegar mixed with 3 tbsp. water
2	tbsp. onion, finely chopped
2	tbsp. coriander, finely chopped
2	tbsp. fresh parsley
	drinking water for beans

1. Place beans in a pot, cover them with drinking water and cook uncovered for 2 hours until beans are tender but still intact. Drain and toss with salt.

2. In a mortar, or food processor, pound or process walnuts with garlic and cayenne. Place in small glass mixing bowl. Stir in vinegar/water mixture until well blended. Add walnut paste, onions, coriander and parsley to beans. Mix well being careful not to bruise beans. May be chilled before serving.

Serves 4

NOTES

LIMA BEAN CASSEROLE

⅔   cup dried lima beans, soaked overnight and drained
2   tbsp. olive oil
1   large green bell pepper, seeded and diced
2   ribs celery, diced
1   large onion, chopped
1   clove garlic, peeled and mashed
½   cup raisins
1½ tbsp. sesame seeds
¾   cup soy "jack" cheese, grated
    drinking water for beans

1. Place beans in a pot, cover them with cold water. Bring water to boil, then simmer, adding just enough water to keep beans covered for two hours or until tender. Drain, reserve cooking liquid.

2. In a large skillet, heat oil. Add green pepper, celery, onion and garlic. Cook over medium heat 10 minutes or until tender. Stir pepper/onion mixture into beans, 1½ cup cooking liquid (add water if necessary), raisins and sesame seeds and half of the cheese.

3. Turn mixture into a large oiled casserole. Bake in a preheated 375° oven for 25 minutes. Sprinkle on remaining cheese, return to oven for 10 minutes to allow cheese to melt and form a bubbly crust.

Serves 4- 6

MUNG BEANS WITH LEMON AND CAPERS

1   cup dried mung beans, soaked in drinking water for 1 hour
¼   cup olive oil
2   medium onions, chopped finely
1   clove garlic, chopped
2   tbsp. capers
1   large lemon, peel grated and juice strained
¼   cup parsley, finely chopped

1. Place beans and soaking water in pot. Bring to boil, then simmer for 40 minutes. Drain if necessary.

2. Heat oil in a large sauce pan over very low heat. Add onions and garlic, cooking until translucent but not browned. Stir in beans, capers, lemon peel and juice. Cover and simmer for 3-5 minutes to blend flavors. Mix in parsley and serve.

Serves 4

BOHEMIAN YELLOW PEAS

2	cups dried yellow peas, soaked overnight and drained
1	sprig fresh thyme or ½ tsp. dried thyme
1	bay leaf
3	whole cloves
4	peppercorns
2	small onions, thinly sliced
1	carrot, scrubbed and chopped finely
6	cups drinking water
6	tbsp. butter
3	tbsp. dry whole bread crumbs sauteed in 2 tsp. butter
1	tsp. sea salt
½	tsp. black pepper

1. Wrap the thyme, bay leaf, cloves, peppercorns and a few slices of the onion in a double layer of cheesecloth. Tie securely. Place the seasoning bag, the carrot and peas in a large pot with the 6 cups of water. Bring to boil. Cook for 1½ hours until the peas are soft. Discard the seasoning bag. Drain peas.

2. Melt butter in a large skillet. Add remaining onions and cook over medium heat until they are translucent but not brown. Set aside.

3. Coat a 6-cup baking dish with remaining butter. Coat with 2 tbsp. dry bread crumbs. Season the peas with salt and pepper. Place in baking dish. Top with sauteed onions, then cover with remaining 1 tbsp. bread crumbs. Bake in a preheated 375° oven for 15 minutes to warm through and crisp top. Serve immediately.

Serves 6

Garbanzo Paté

2	cups garbanzo beans, cooked
⅓	cup freshly squeezed lemon juice
2	tbsp. tahini
2	tbsp. tamari
1	tsp. vegesal
1	tsp. cumin, ground
1	cup short grained brown rice, cooked
½	cup almonds, toasted and finely chopped
½	cup finely chopped yellow onion
½	cup finely chopped fresh parsley
2	tbsp. sesame seeds
1	tsp. olive oil

1. Rinse and drain cooked garbanzo beans. Process in food processor with lemon juice, tahini, tamari, vegesal and cumin until a smooth consistency is reached.

2. Transfer garbanzo mixture to medium-sized bowl. Add rice, almonds, onions, parsley and sesame seeds. Mix well to combine all ingredients.

3. Brush inside of mold or loaf pan with olive oil. Pat pate mixture into pan using slight pressure to remove any air pockets. Refrigerate for at least two hours before unmolding to serve.

This pate is a delicious appetizer served with crackers, but also provides a good protein combination when sliced and served on a bed of fresh greens.

Serves 4- 6

Tofu Stew

½	cup safflower oil
2	onions, sliced
2	cloves garlic
2	carrots, scrubbed and coarselychopped
½	lb. green cabbage, coarsely chopped
2	tofu cakes, sliced into 16 equal pieces
½	lb. green beans, trimmed
1	cup drinking water
½	cup soy sauce

1. Heat oil in large casserole. Add onions and garlic. Cook until soft but not browned. Add carrots and cabbage. Saute for 1 minute more.

2. Add tofu, green beans, water and soy sauce. Gently bring mixture to boil for 15-20 minutes, until the juices thicken slightly.

Serves 6

TOFU WITH ANKAKE SAUCE

SAUCE

⅔   **cup vegetable stock or water**

3   **tbsp. tamari**

2   **tbsp. raw honey**

2   **tsp. cornstarch, dissolved in 2 tbsp. water**

2   **tsp. fresh ginger, peeled and grated**

1   **tsp. fresh orange peel, grated**

TOFU

⅓   **cup cornstarch**

¼   **cup drinking water**

12   **oz. extra firm tofu**

2-4 **tbsp. safflower oil**

1. For the sauce, combine stock or water, tamari and honey in a small sauce pan. Bring to boil. Stir in cornstarch, ginger and orange peel. Cook for 1 minute until thick. Keep warm while preparing the tofu.

2. For the tofu, combine cornstarch and water in a small bowl. Cut tofu into 12 thin rectangles, dip them in batter. Heat oil in a large skillet. Saute tofu slices taking care not to put too many in at once. Cook until golden brown. Drain briefly on a wire rack, then transfer to an absorbent paper towel. Place tofu slices on warmed platter topped with sauce. Serve immediately.

Serves 4

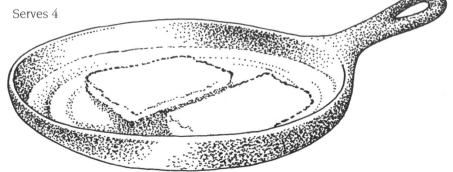

Tempeh Mole

½   cup raw cashews
1   cup red pimento peppers or red bells
1   cup tomato paste
½   cup drinking water
¼   cup carob powder
1   tbsp. chili powder
1½ tsp. cinnamon
1   clove garlic
½   small onion
2   12 oz. tempeh

1. Place all ingredients except tempeh in blender. Process until smooth, adding additional water if too thick. Transfer to sauce pan and cook over low heat, stirring frequently to prevent sticking for 10 minutes.

2. Meanwhile, cut tempeh into 2" cubes. Place in a large, heavy bottomed sauce pan. Pour mole sauce over tempeh. Turn heat to medium and gently warm until tempeh is heated through. Serve with brown rice.

Serves 4- 6

Sweet and Sour Tempeh

2   12 oz. tempeh
4   tbsp. tamari
½   cup almonds, slivered
1   large onion, sliced into thin wedges
1   green bell pepper, seeded and sliced lengthwise
1   red bell pepper, seeded and sliced lengthwise
1   large carrot, scrubbed and sliced thinly on the diagonal
1   stalk celery, sliced thinly on diagonal
1   cup fresh pineapple, cut into small pieces
1½ tbsp. raw honey
2   tbsp. apple cider vinegar
1½ cups vegetable stock or water
1½ tbsp. arrowroot

1. Cut tempeh into 2" cubes and marinate in 2 tbsp. of tamari. Meanwhile, toast almonds in a dry skillet, over low heat until just golden. Set aside.

2. In a wok, or other large skillet, stir fry onions, peppers, carrots and celery in ¼ cup stock or water until just tender. Add pineapple.

3. Mix together honey, vinegar, 1 cup of stock or water. Add to vegetable along with tempeh. Continue cooking over medium heat for 1 minute.

4. Dissolve arrowroot in remaining ¼ cup of liquid and 2 tbsp. of tamari. Stir into tempeh mixture. Allow to continue cooking 1-2 minutes longer to allow sauce to thicken and clear. Serve over brown rice.

Serves 6

LENTILS WITH LEMON & CHARD

1½	cups dried lentils
	drinking water
2½	lb. chard, stems removed but a few reserved and chopped with the leaves
¾	cup olive oil
1	medium onion, chopped
⅓	cup celery, chopped
2	cloves garlic, peeled and mashed
1	tsp. whole wheat pastry flour
¾	cup fresh lemon juice
1½	tsp. sea salt
1	tsp. pepper

1. In a large pot, cook lentils in enough water to cover for 15-20 minutes until tender. Add chard and cook another 10 minutes.

2. Meanwhile, heat oil in a skillet. Add onions, celery and garlic. Saute until translucent. Stir in flour and lemon juice. Add this mixture to the lentils. Season with salt and pepper. Simmer 10-15 minutes until sauce has thickened.

Serves 6

LENTIL PUMPKIN STEW

2   tbsp. safflower oil
2   onions, sliced
1   dried hot red chili
1   tsp. paprika
1   tsp. sea salt
8   cups drinking water
2   cups dried lentils
2   lb. pumpkin or other winter squash, peeled, seeded and cubed
3   tomatoes, seeded and chopped

1. In a large pot, heat oil. Add onion, chili, paprika and salt. Saute until onions are soft but not browned. Add water. Bring mixture to a boil. Add lentils. Simmer for 15 minutes.

2. Add pumpkin and tomatoes. Continue cooking for 15-20 minutes more until pumpkin is tender. Add a little water if stew becomes too thick.

Serves 6

LENTILS WITH WALNUTS AND APRICOTS

1   cup dried lentils
     drinking water
3   tbsp. butter
½   cup dried apricots, soaked in warm water for 15 minutes and drained
1   large onion, finely chopped
1   tsp. sea salt
1   tsp. black pepper
¼   cup pomegranite seeds
¼   cup walnuts, chopped
2   tbsp. parsley, finely chopped

1. Place lentils in large sauce pan, covering with water. Bring to boil. Place lid on pot and simmer over low heat for 15-20 minutes until lentils are tender. Drain and return to pan.

2. In large skillet, heat butter. Add apricots and onions. Cook over low heat until onions begin to soften. Season mixture with salt and pepper. Add onion mixture, pomegranite seeds and walnuts to lentils. Place sauce pan over very low heat for 8-10 minutes to heat lentils through without drying out. Place in serving dish and top with parsley.

Serves 4

BROWN RICE WITH ALMONDS & MUSHROOMS

1	cup long grained brown rice
2	tsp. sea salt
2½	cups vegetable broth
1	large onion, diced
3	stalks celery, chopped
¼	cup cold pressed vegetable oil
½	cup almonds, slivered
1	tbsp. fresh sage or 1 tsp. rubbed dry
½	tsp. dried marjoram or rosemary
½	lb. mushrooms, brushed clean with a vegetable brush and sliced

1. Combine rice, sea salt and broth in a heavy duty pan. Bring to boil and stir. Cover and reduce heat to a low simmer for 50 minutes or until rice is tender and liquid is absorbed.

2. Meanwhile, saute onion and celery in oil until translucent but not browned. Add almonds and continue to cook for 3 minutes stirring frequently so the nuts do not burn. Add herbs and mushrooms. Continue to saute until mushrooms are wilted. Combine with rice and mix well.

3. This dish may be kept warm in a 350° oven.

Serves 4

SAVORY RICE

1   cup brown basmati or long grained rice
2½   cups vegetable broth
2   tbsp. raw sesame seeds
1   tsp. vegesal
⅔   cup raw cashews
2   tbsp. butter
¼   cup parsley, chopped
1   tbsp. tamari

1. Combine rice and broth in a heavy duty pan. Bring to boil and stir. Cover and reduce heat to a low simmer for 50 minutes or until rice is tender and liquid is absorbed.

2. In a deep skillet, pan toast sesame seeds with ½ tsp. of vegesal. Cook over medium heat until golden brown. The entire process takes less than 2 minutes. Add cashews and continue to toast in dry skillet until nuts begin to brown.

3. Add butter, cooked rice and parsley. Stir together and heat for 5 minutes over medium heat. Add tamari just before serving.

A delicious variation to this recipe would be to use freshly squeezed lemon juice in place of the tamari.

Serves 4

SPANISH RICE

1   cup short grained brown rice
1   medium onion, finely chopped
1   tsp. cold pressed vegetable oil
1   tsp. sea salt
⅛   tsp. cayenne pepper
2½   cups vegetable broth
1   large green bell pepper, diced
3   medium tomatoes, seeded and chopped
1   tbsp. fresh oregano or ½ tsp. dry
1   tbsp. fresh basil or ½ tsp. dry
1   cup fresh or frozen peas

1. Combine rice, onions, oil, salt and cayenne and broth in a large heavy pan. Bring to a boil and stir. Cover and reduce heat to a low simmer for 15 minutes.

2. Add peppers, tomatoes and herbs. Simmer for another 30-35 minutes until rice is tender and all liquid is absorbed. Toss with fork to fluff.

3. Add peas. Stir to heat through and serve.

Serves 4-6

NEPALESE RICE

¼   cup flaxseed or safflower oil
8   scallions, sliced
1   2 inch cinnamon stick
4   whole cloves
1   tsp. sea salt
¼   tsp. turmeric
1   cup brown, short grained rice, soaked for 45 minutes and drained
1   cup drinking water, hot
2½   cups coconut milk
4   sprigs cilantro

1. Heat oil in a large skillet. Add scallions and saute until crisp. Remove from heat and drain on paper towels.

2. Add cinnamon, cloves, sea salt, turmeric and rice to pan. Continue cooking over medium high heat for 3 minutes. Add hot water and coconut milk. Cover pan and cook mixture for 40 minutes until rice is tender. Stir in cilantro and place skillet, uncovered in a preheated 300° oven for 10 minutes to remove excess moisture.

3. Transfer rice to serving dish. Top with scallions and serve immediately.

Serves 4

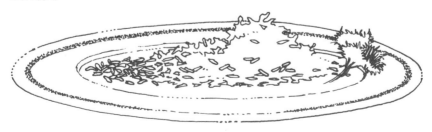

SPINACH RICE

2   tbsp. butter

1   small onion, chopped

1   cup brown rice

½   cup tomato sauce

2   cups drinking water

2   lb. fresh spinach, washed, stems removed and torn

¼   cup parsley, chopped

1   tbsp. mint, chopped

1   tsp. sea salt

½   tsp. black pepper

¼   tsp. nutmeg, ground

1   lemon, cut in wedges

4   eggs, hard boiled (optional-San Pasqual inoculated eggs only)

1. In a large enameled pan, heat butter. Add onions, cooking until translucent but not browned. Add rice and continue cooking for 3 minutes, stirring constantly. Add tomato sauce and water. Cover and simmer until rice is almost tender about 35 minutes.

2. Uncover pan, mix in spinach, parsley, mint, salt and pepper. Partially cover pan and continue cooking until spinach is wilted. Add nutmeg. Continue cooking until rice is fully tender and liquid has been absorbed.

3. Transfer to a serving dish. Garnish with lemon wedges and sliced eggs if used. Serve warm.

Serves 4- 6

NOTES

NUTTED PILAF

4   tbsp. butter

1   cup brown, long grained rice

½   tsp. sea salt

2½   cups drinking water or vegetable broth, heated to boiling in small sauce pan

⅓   cup currants

1   tbsp. fresh orange peel, grated

½   cup pine nuts or slivered almonds

2   tbsp. parsley, chopped finely

1. Melt 2 tbsp. of butter in large sauce pan. Add rice and salt. Cook for 3 minutes, stirring constantly. Add boiling water or vegetable broth. Cover and simmer for 45 minutes until rice is tender. Remove from heat, stir in currants and orange peel. Toss with fork to fluff rice.

2. Heat remaining butter in skillet. Add nuts and toast lightly over very low heat. Pour nuts over rice and gently mix. Transfer rice to serving dish and garnish with parsley.

Serves 4

WILD RICE AND FRESH PEAS

3   tbsp. butter

½   cup almonds, slivered

4   cups cooked wild rice

2   cups fresh peas

1   tbsp. orange peel, finely grated

1. Preheat oven to 325°. Melt butter in 2 quart casserole. Add almonds tossing until well coated. Place in oven for 10 minutes, stirring occasionally until almonds are lightly toasted.

2. Add rice, peas and orange peel. Mix well. Return to oven, covered for 15-18 minutes until heated through.

Serves 6

CARROT AND WILD RICE CASSEROLE

1	tbsp. flaxseed or safflower oil
1	large onion, chopped
4	cups cooked wild rice
2	cups carrot, finely chopped
¼	cup pecans
1	tsp. sea salt
1	cup cream
1½	tsp. egg replacer mixed in 2 tbsp. water

1. Heat oil in skillet. Add onions, cooking over medium heat until onions are translucent but not browned.

2. Add wild rice, carrots, pecans and salt to onions. Mix well.

3. Combine cream and egg replacer in a small bowl. Fold into rice mixture.

4. Turn mixture into a buttered 2 quart casserole. Bake, covered, in preheated 350° oven for 30 minutes. Remove cover and stir well. Continue baking for 10 minutes more until rice is firm.

Serves 4-6

MILLET HASH WITH MUSHROOMS

4	cups drinking water
2	cups millet
3	tbsp. butter
1	cup cashews, chopped
1½	cups onions, chopped
2½	lb. mushrooms, brushed clean with a vegetable brush and coarsely chopped
1	tsp. sea salt
1½	tsp. mint, finely chopped

1. Bring water to boil in large pot. Add millet. Simmer for 15 minutes until millet is half cooked.

2. Meanwhile in a large skillet, heat butter over medium heat. Add cashews. Cook for 2-3 minutes. Add onions and cook for 2-3 minutes more.

3. Stir mushroom mixture in millet. Pour mixture into a shallow, buttered 8" baking dish. Season with salt. Bake uncovered in a preheated 350° oven for 45 minutes until hash is dry and crispy. Top with mint and serve.

Serves 4

SYRIAN CRACKED WHEAT BANADOORA

¼ **cup extra virgin olive oil**
½ **cup onion, chopped**
1 **cup mushrooms, brushed clean with a vegetable brush and sliced**
1½ **cups cracked wheat**
2½ **cups vegetable broth**
½ **cup tomato sauce**
1 **tsp. sea salt**
½ **tsp. black pepper**
1 **tbsp. lemon juice**
1 **tsp. fresh dill or ½ tsp. dried**
½ **tsp. mint, freshly chopped**
½ **tsp. cumin (optional)**

1. Heat oil in large skillet. Add onions. Cook until translucent but not browned. Add mushrooms, continue cooking over medium heat until all liquid has been absorbed.

2. Add cracked wheat, broth, tomato sauce, salt and pepper. Cook, covered, over very low heat for 15-20 minutes until liquid is absorbed. Stir in lemon juice, dill, mint and cumin. Serve warm or at room temperature.

Serves 4-6

BIBLICAL "CORN"

4   tbsp. butter
1   large onion, chopped
¼   cup millet
¼   cup pearl barley
¼   cup lentils
¼   cup cracked wheat
1   tsp. sea salt
¼   tsp. cumin
2   cups drinking water or vegetable broth

1. Heat butter in large sauce pan over medium heat. Add onions. Cook
   until translucent but not browned. Add millet, barley, lentils, cracked
   wheat, salt, cumin and water. Cover with a tight fitting lid and cook
   over very low heat for 20 minutes. Remove cover, continue cooking for
   5 minutes longer, stirring frequently to prevent sticking.

Serves 4

NOTES

DESSERTS

DESSERTS
FRUITS, BAKED GOODS AND SPECIAL DELIGHTS

Let's face it -- a lot of diets can bore you to tears and take all the joy out of dining. We have taken great pains to develop a variety of healthful yet *tasty* desserts for the end of your meal.

First of all, the best and easiest dessert is fresh fruit in season, served attractively. But of course, there are those times when the whole family is coming together for dinner or special guests are arriving and you want to prepare something really memorable. Since we expect you to fully enjoy your new way of life, we present several unusually tasty ways to enjoy dessert without consuming refined sugar, white flour, or egg products.

Fruit remains the mainstay of the desserts offered in this section; however, carob powder, tofu and arrowroot, along with whole wheat flour, can transform ordinary fruits into extraordinarily delicious desserts.

As always, begin your recipe with the finest ingredients available. No shortcuts. You should choose fruit that is organically grown, fully ripened before picking, and as unblemished as possible. When preparing the recipe, use the whole fruit, including the skin. Nuts called for in recipes should be raw. Dried fruits must be of the unsulphured variety found in every health food store.

Feel free to create your own arrowroot puddings experimenting with other natural flavorings such as mint, fresh fruits and natural extracts. The rule of thumb for these puddings is two tablespoons arrowroot for each cup of liquid. Cream is called for in many recipes, but usually as only a topping. Feel free to substitute either tofu cream (the recipe is at the back of the section) or a nut cream from the *Beverage* section if you are including cream elsewhere in your menu. As with all recipes in the book, spices have been added for maximum flavor value but may be adjusted to your own palate.

DRIED FRUIT COMPOTE

1   **cup dried apples, unsulphured**
1   **cup dried apricots, unsulphured**
1   **cup prunes, unsulphured**
½   **cup golden raisins**
8   **cups drinking water**
2   **cinnamon sticks**
½   **cup sunflower seeds**
¼   **cup almonds, slivered and toasted**
1   **cup whipped cream sweetened with 1 tbsp. apple juice**

1. In a large sauce pan, combine all fruits, sunflower seeds and cinnamon sticks with water. Bring to a boil. Lower heat, cover pan with lid and simmer slowly for 45 minutes. Compote may be served hot, room temperature or chilled.

2. Top with almonds and whipped cream.

Serves 4-6

FRUIT POPS

3   **cups frozen fruit such as fresh peaches, apricot, mangoes, papayas or any berry**
1   **cup drinking water**
1   **tbsp. honey**

1. Blend fruit, honey and water in blender until smooth. Pour into popsicle molds and freeze.

Makes 4 cups, number pops depends on mold size

FRUIT SORBET

2 cups frozen fruit or berries
2 tsp. fresh lime juice

1. Place fruit in juicer with blank blade instead of screen. Blend in lime juice. Press puree through sieve placed over fruit cups.

Serves 4-6

FROZEN PEACH DELIGHT

1 cup apple juice
½ cup almond butter
1 tsp. vanilla
2 cups fresh peachs, frozen
3 bananas, cut into pieces and frozen

1. Place juice, almond butter and vanilla in blender. Blend until smooth. Add frozen fruit ½ cup at a time ending with the frozen bananas. This will thicken the mixture. Pour into chilled parfait glasses or custard cups. Serve at once.

Makes 4-6 servings

FROZEN CURRANT PECAN DELIGHT

1 cup pineapple juice
¾ cup pecans
¾ cup currants
2 cups frozen pineapple, apricots or peaches
2 bananas, cut into pieces and frozen

1. Place pineapple juice, pecans and currants in blender. Blend until smooth. Add frozen fruit ½ cup at a time ending with the frozen bananas. This will thicken the mixture. Pour into chilled parfait glasses or custard cups. Serve at once.

Serves 4-6

STRAWBERRY BANANA CUSTARD

4   ripe bananas, cut into pieces
1   tbsp. lime juice
2   cups strawberries, sliced or 1-16 oz. package frozen
     strawberries, thawed
2   cups drinking water
½   cup quick cooking tapioca

1. Place bananas and lime juice in blender. Blend until smooth. Place in
   medium sauce pan. Add berries and their juice, tapioca and water. Mix
   well. Let stand for 5 minutes. Heat fruit mixture to boiling, stirring
   constantly. Remove from heat. Let stand for 20-25 minutes to thicken.
   Serve in custard cups. May be topped with tofu cream and nuts
   if desired.

Serves 6

PAPAYA MELBA

½   cup strawberries, halved lengthwise
½   cup blueberries
½   cup raspberries
½   cup pineapple, crushed
2   tbsp. raw honey
2   tbsp. lime juice
3   papayas, halved and seeded

1. In mixing bowl, combine berries, pineapple, honey and lime juice. Stir
   gently. Let stand 15 minutes to allow juices to blend.

2. Arrange papaya halves on dessert
   dishes or platter. Top each
   half with a generous
   scoop of berry
   mixture. May be
   served with
   whipped cream or
   tofu cream and
   sunflower seeds if desired.

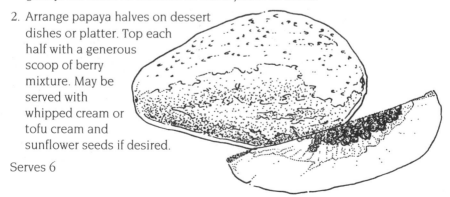

Serves 6

LEMON PUDDING

5   tbsp. arrowroot
2   cups drinking water
½   tsp. raw honey
1   tbsp. fresh lemon juice
1   tsp. lemon peel, finely grated

1. Stir arrowroot into ½ cup cold water.

2. Bring remaining water to boil in medium sauce pan. Add arrowroot mixture, stirring over medium-high heat for 5 minutes until mixture clears and thickens.

3. Remove from heat and add honey, lemon juice and lemon peel. Stir well. Cool in refrigerator at least ½ hour until set.

Serves 4

CHERRY PUDDING

5   tbsp. arrowroot
2   cups drinking water
½   tsp. raw honey
1   tbsp. cherry juice concentrate
1   tsp. lemon peel, finely grated

1. Stir arrowroot into ½ cup cold water.

2. Bring remaining water to boil in medium sauce pan. Add arrowroot mixture, stirring over medium-high heat for 5 minutes until mixture clears and thickens.

3. Remove from heat and add honey, cherry juice and lemon peel. Cool in refrigerator at least ½ hour until set.

Serves 4

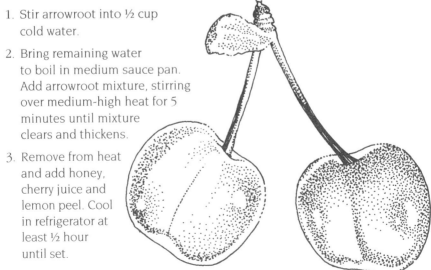

APPLE PUDDING

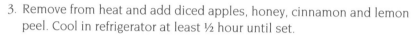

5	tbsp. arrowroot
½	cup drinking water
1½	cups fresh apple juice
½	cup apple, finely diced
½	tsp. raw honey
½	tsp. cinnamon
1	tsp. lemon peel, finely grated

1. Stir arrowroot into ½ cup cold water.

2. Bring apple juice to boil in medium sauce pan. Add arrowroot mixture, stirring over medium-high heat for 5 minutes until mixture clears and thickens.

3. Remove from heat and add diced apples, honey, cinnamon and lemon peel. Cool in refrigerator at least ½ hour until set.

Serves 4

CAROB PUDDING

5	tbsp. arrowroot
3	tbsp. carob powder
2	cups drinking water
½	tsp. raw honey
1	tsp. orange peel, finely chopped

1. Stir arrowroot and carob powder into ½ cup cold water.

2. Bring remaining water to boil in medium sauce pan. Add arrowroot mixture, stirring over medium-high heat for 5 minutes until mixture clears and thickens.

3. Remove from heat and add honey and orange peel. Cool in refrigerator at least ½ hour until set.

Serves 4

SWEET POTATO CUSTARD

4   ripe bananas
1½ cups sweet potatoes, boiled or baked until soft
½   cup apple juice
1   tsp. vanilla
½   tsp. cinnamon

1. Mash bananas until smooth and creamy. Fold in cooked sweet potatoes until well blended. Add apple juice, vanilla and cinnamon. Serve in custard cups.

Serves 4

BAVARIAN CREAM WITH STRAWBERRIES

3   tbsp. natural vegetable gelatin
1   cup drinking water, hot
2   cups strawberries, fresh or frozen
3   tbsp. raw honey
½   cup cream

1. Soften gelatin in ½ cup of hot water. Set aside.

2. Place remaining ½ cup of water in blender with strawberries and honey. Blend on low speed. Pour gelatin slowly into mixture and continue blending for 30 seconds.

3. Whip cream until it forms peaks. Fold cream into strawberry mixture. Pour into a glass bowl or mold and chill until firm.

Serves 4

BANANA SPLIT

1	tbsp. butter
1	cup carob powder
½	cup soy milk or 50% diluted cream
1	tbsp. raw honey
4	ripe bananas
1	cup strawberries, sliced
1	cup fresh pineapple, cut into bite size pieces
1	cup cream, whipped with 1 tsp. vanilla
½	cup nuts, chopped
¼	cup raw unsweetened coconut
¼	cup carob chips

1. Melt butter in a medium sauce pan on low heat. Add carob powder and melt slowly, stirring constantly. Add soy milk or diluted cream. Whip until smooth. Remove from heat and beat in honey. Set aside, but keep warm.

2. Slice bananas lengthwise and place in dessert bowls. Pour carob sauce over bananas. Distribute strawberries and pineapple evenly over each portion, then whipped cream. Sprinkle with nuts, coconut flakes and carob chips. Serve.

Serves 4

NOTES

RAW FUDGE

½   cup butter or almond butter
1   tbsp. vanilla
⅓   cup almond milk
1   cup carob powder
⅓   cup arrowroot
1   cup unsweetened grated coconut
1   cup walnuts, chopped

1. In a mixing bowl, cream butter with vanilla until light. Slowly add almond milk.

2. Mix carob powder and arrowroot together. Add these dry ingredients to arrowroot mixture, beating well. You may have to add an additional tbsp. of almond milk if mixture is too dry.

3. Fold in coconut and walnuts. Press entire mixture into 8"x8" buttered dish or form into balls the size of small walnuts. Chill to set.

Makes 24 pieces

CAROB OATMEAL COOKIES

½   cup pitted dates
2   tbsp. butter
½   cup rolled oats
1   cup buckwheat
½   tsp. sea salt
3   ripe bananas
1   tsp. vanilla
½   cup carob chips

1. Process dates and butter together in food processor. Place in small sauce pan and cook over low heat for 3-5 minutes until mixture is well blended. Cool.

2. Preheat oven to 375°. Place oats in food processor. Process to form oat flour. Combine in medium bowl with buckwheat flour and salt. Set aside.

3. In a large mixing bowl, mash bananas until smooth. Blend in date butter and vanilla until smooth. Stir in flour mixture. Fold in carob chips.

4. Using a mixing spoon, make 1" mounds on non-stick baking sheet. Bake 12-15 minutes until lightly browned.

Makes 2 dozen cookies

PINEAPPLE DATE BAR COOKIES

FILLING
1   cup dates, chopped
½   cup fresh pineapple, crushed
¾   cup pineapple juice

BAR LAYER
1½   cups rolled oats
1½   cups oat flour
2   tbsp. sesame seeds
2   tsp. baking powder
½   tsp. cinnamon
2   tsp. vanilla
1½   tsp. egg replacer mixed with 2 tbsp. water
1   tbsp. apple juice
¼   cup butter

1. Pre heat oven to 350°. Place dates, pineapple and pineapple juice together in sauce pan. Cook over medium-low heat until moisture is absorbed. Remove from heat.

2. Mix oats, oat flour, sesame seeds and baking powder together. Add all other ingredients, mixing well. Pat one half of bar mixture into the bottom of an 8" square buttered baking pan. layer with date filling. Sprinkle remaining oat mixture on top.

3. Bake 30 minutes. Allow to stand at least 1 hour before cutting into bars.

Makes 24 bars

SESAME OATMEAL COOKIES

3	cups oatmeal
½	cup honey
½	cup apple juice
1	cup walnuts, roughly chopped
1½	cups tahini
1	tsp. cinnamon
½	tsp. nutmeg

1. Preheat oven to 350°.

2. Mix all ingredients together well. Drop by spoonfuls onto nonstick baking sheet. Bake 10-12 minutes until edges are brown. Cool.

Makes 2 dozen cookies

ALMOND CRISPS

¼	cup butter
⅔	cup almond butter
½	cup maple syrup
1⅓	cups whole wheat pastry flour
1	tsp. baking powder

1. Preheat oven to 350°. Cream together butter, almond butter and syrup. Add dry ingredients, mixing well.

2. Roll into small balls and place on buttered cookie sheet. Bake 12-15 minutes until edges are brown. Cool on racks to allow maximum crisping.

Makes 4 dozen

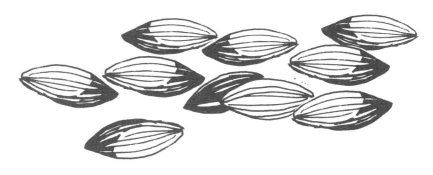

APPLE RAISIN BARS

½   cup apple sauce
½   cup apple juice
4   tbsp. butter, melted
4½   tsp. egg replacer mixed with 6 tbsp. water
2   cups whole wheat pastry flour
3   tsp. baking powder
1   tsp. sea salt
2   tsp. cinnamon
1   tsp. nutmeg
1   cup raisins or currants

1. Preheat oven to 350°. In a large mixing bowl, combine apple sauce, apple juice, butter and egg replacer. Mix flour, baking powder, salt, cinnamon and nutmeg together. Fold into apple mixture. Fold in raisins or currants.

2. Press mixture into buttered 8" square baking pan. Bake 25 minutes.

Makes 16 squares

ALMOND ORANGE MEDJOOLS

½   cup almond butter
½   tsp. raw honey
½   cup unsweetened coconut, shredded
1   tsp. orange peel, freshly grated
8   large medjool dates

1. Mix almond butter and honey together until smooth. Stir in coconut and orange peel.

2. Split dates lengthwise down center and spread open for filling. Place 1 tbsp. filling in each date. Serve.

Serves 8

BEE-LICIOUS BARS

1	cup cashew butter
1	cup raw honey
1	cup carob powder
1	cup sunflower seeds
⅔	cup granola
½	cup almonds, chopped
½	cup raisins, preferably golden
½	cup unsweetened coconut, shredded
4	tbsp. bee pollen granules
1	tsp. sesame seeds

1. In a medium sauce pan, heat cashew butter and honey over low heat, stirring until smooth. Remove from heat.

2. Stir in remaining ingredients. Press into an 8" square baking pan. Chill, cut into squares.

Makes 16 squares

COCOMINT CREAM TORTE

4	tbsp. butter, melted
2	cups granola
4	cups soft tofu
1	cup carob powder
½	cup raw honey
½	tsp. mint extract

1. Mix melted butter with granola. Press into the bottom of an 8" or 9" springform pan. Bake at 400° for 8-10 minutes. Cool.

2. Meanwhile, drain tofu in a strainer for 15 minutes. Press to remove excess liquid. Blend tofu with carob powder, honey and mint extract until smooth. If the tofu is very soft, you may have to add a bit more to thicken. Pour over crust. Chill for at least two hours or overnight for best results. Top with whipped cream flavored with honey and vanilla.

Serves 8-10

TOFU CHEESECAKE

2	cups granola
¼	cup apple juice
48	oz. tofu
4	tbsp. raw honey
1	cup soy milk
½	cup tahini
2	tsp. fresh lemon juice
1	tsp. vanilla
½	tsp. sea salt

1. Mix granola with apple juice. Press into the bottom of an 8" or 9" springform pan. Bake at 400° for 8-10 minutes. Cool.

2. Meanwhile, drain tofu and press to remove excess liquid. Place in blender with honey, soy milk, tahini, lemon juice, vanilla and sea salt. Blend until smooth. Pour filling into springform pan. Bakes at 325° for 30 minutes. When center of cake is firm, turn off heat and let cake remain in oven for another 30 minutes. Allow to cool then refrigerate overnight. Flavor is best when allowed to rest for 2 days.

Serves 12

NOTES

CARROT FRUITCAKE

1	cup carrots, scrubbed and grated
1	cup currants
¾	cup raw honey
2	tbsp. butter
1	tsp. cinnamon
1	tsp. allspice
1	tsp. nutmeg
¼	tsp. cloves, ground
1½	cups drinking water
1½	cups whole wheat flour
½	cup wheat germ
1	tsp. baking soda
½	cup walnuts

1. Preheat oven to 350°. In a medium sauce pan, place carrots, currants, honey, butter, spices and water. Bring to a boil, then simmer for 10 minutes. Cool.

2. In a large mixing bowl, mix together flour, wheat germ, baking soda and walnuts. Stir in carrot mixture. Pour batter into two small, buttered loaf pans. Bake for 45 minutes until toothpick comes out clean.

Makes 2 small loaves

APPLE CRISP

8	large green apples, sliced
¾	cup raw honey
2	tsp. lemon juice
2	tsp. cinnamon
½	tsp. allspice
1½	cups whole wheat pastry flour
8	tbsp. unsalted butter
½	cup walnut pieces
½	tsp. sea salt

1. Preheat oven to 350°. In a large bowl, mix together in a bowl sliced apples, ½ cup of honey, lemon juice, cinnamon and allspice. In a separate bowl, mix until crumbly flour, butter, walnuts and sea salt.

2. Layer ½ of the apple mixture in a 9x12, buttered baking pan. Top with half of crumb mixture. Repeat layers making sure that crumb topping covers all apples. Bake for 30 minutes until apples are barely tender. Drizzle remaining honey over topping. Return to oven for 10 more minutes until apples are tender.

Serves 8

PEAR PIE

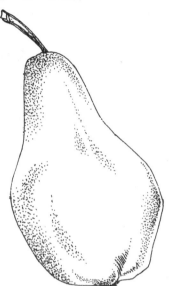

1½	**cups whole wheat flour**
½	**cup wheat germ**
¾	**tsp. sea salt**
10	**tbsp. butter, chilled**
	cold water
8	**ripe pears**
½	**cup fresh orange juice**
2	**tbsp. arrowroot**
½	**tsp. coriander, ground**
½	**tsp. anise**
½	**tsp. cinnamon**
½	**tsp. nutmeg**
¼	**tsp. sea salt**
1	**tsp. vanilla**

1. Stir together flour, wheat germ and salt. Use a pastry cutter or two knives to cut in butter. Continue cutting until mixture resembles coarse meal. Sprinkle with just enough cold water to hold dough together. Gently form dough into ball. On a lightly floured surface, press dough to make a thick disk. Roll on this surface or between two sheets of waxed paper. Place rolled dough in 9" pie pan, shape a rim with your fingers. Refrigerate for at least 2 hours for flakiest pie crust.

2. While pie crust is chilling, peel and core pears. Heat orange juice and arrowroot in a sauce pan with spices and vanilla until clear.

3. Toss orange juice mixture with sliced pears. Place in chilled pie crust. Bake at 350° for 35-45 minutes until pears are tender and pie crust is evenly browned.

Serves 6-8

ANY BERRY PIE

1⅓ cups cashews, ground

⅓ cup sesame seeds, ground

⅔ cup butter, softened

1½ tsp. natural gelatin

2 tbsp. water, boiling

1 pint fresh berries, any variety or a mixture such as half raspberry and half black berry

2 tbsp. raw honey

2 tsp. lemon juice

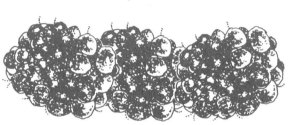

1. Mix together cashews, sesame seeds and butter until crumbly. Pat into 8"x9" pie pan.

2. Dissolve gelatin in 2 tbsp. of boiling water in small glass bowl.

3. Place 1 cup berries and honey in blender. Blend just until berries are liquefied. Add lemon juice and gelatin. Continue to blend.

4. Meanwhile, place remaining berries on top of seed crust. Pour blended mixture over top. Refrigerate to set at least 2 hours. Serve with whipped cream or tofu cream.

Serves 6-8

"FREEZER COOKED" APPLE PIE

1⅓ cup cashews, ground

⅔ cup sesame seeds

⅓ cup tahini

8 green apples, cored

½ cup pineapple juice

1 tsp. natural gelatin

1 cup fresh apple juice

½ tsp. cinnamon

½ tsp. nutmeg

1. Mix together cashews, sesame seeds and tahini. Pat ½ of mixture into 9" pie pan.

2. Slice apples, dipping immediately into pineapple juice to prevent discoloring. Layer in pie pan over crust. Place in freezer for at least 4 hours or overnight.

3. In a small sauce pan, mix together gelatin and ¼ cup apple juice. Heat over lowest heat, stirring until gelatin has dissolved and liquid is clear.

4. In a blender, blend remaining apple juice, cinnamon and nutmeg. While running, add gelatin mixture. Pour this mixture over the frozen pie. This gives the frozen apples a "cooked" texture upon thawing. Juice will over cold apples in pie. Top with remaining crust mixture. Serve with whipped cream or tofu cream.

Serves 6-8

TOFU CREAM

8 oz. soft tofu
½ cup rice malt syrup
1 tbsp. cold pressed safflower oil
1 tsp. vanilla
⅛ tsp. sea salt

1. Drain tofu in strainer for 15 minutes. Combine all ingredients in blender and process until smooth. Options include substituting citrus rind or other extract for vanilla.

Makes 1½ cups

WHIPPED CREAM

1 cup heavy cream
1 tbsp. honey
1 tsp. vanilla

1. In a chilled mixing bowl, beat cream until thickened to form soft peaks. Add honey and vanilla. Continue beating until stiff peaks form. Do not over beat, as cream quickly turns to butter.

Makes 1 cup

INDEX

D

O

Oatmeal:
    apple muffins, 57
    cookies, carob, 230
    cookies, sesame, 232
Old Fashioned Dutch Cereal, 50
Olive:
    black, artichoke sandwich, 82
    salsa, moroccan lemon and 119
Olive Paste, bruschetta with, 80
Omelet, spinach, 61
Onion, red, tomato and tofu salad, 110
Orange, medjools, almond, 233
Oriental, salad, rising sun, 105

P

Pancakes:
    apple cakes, 53
    banana nut, 53
    blueberry, 54
    Johnny meal cakes, 55
    sourdough buckwheat, 54
Panothenic acid, 25
Papaya:
    mango salsa, 118
    melba, 225
    mint tea, 36
Parran, Thomas, 2
Pasta: 151-171
    artichoke, 154
    capellini with mushrooms and
      lemon, 156
    cool buckwheat noodles with
      cucumbers, 155
    eggplant, 169
    fettuccine with peas and mint, 164
    fresca, 151
    fusilli with leeks, 167
    mixed herb, 157
    penne with golden garlic, 161
    penne with zucchini and cream, 162
    primavera, 158
    salad, quick artichoke, 102
    soba with Chinese mushrooms, 161
    spinach spaghetti with mushrooms
      and cream, 160
    tagliatelle with broad beans, 153
    tubetti with tomato and avocado
      sauce, 152
    verde, 151
    with almond & green tomato
      sauce,163
    with cauliflower and sun dried
      tomatoes, 170
    with fennel and tomatoes, 165
    with garbanzos, 163
    with potatoes and tomatoes, 171
    with spinach and potatoes, 165
    with summer vegetables, 153
    with sweet pepper sauce, 159
    with sweet potatoes, 166
    with uncooked tomato sauce, 156
    with walnuts, 167
Paté, garbanzo, 208
Pauling, Linus, 23
PC (see Progenitor Cryptocides)
Pea(s):
    fresh, minted soup, 132
    fresh, wild rice and, 217
    snow, Japanese, 186
    split, chilled soup, 136
Peach:
    blossom tea, 37
    frozen delight, 224
Pear:
    breakfast rolls, 60
    pie, 237
    soup, chilled watercress, 135
Pecan:
    frozen currant delight, 224
    spinach salad, 108
Pepper(s):
    carrot soup with, 142
    red, and chili sandwich, 74
    sweet, with tomatoes, 192
Pie:
    any berry, 238
    "freezer cooked" apple, 238
    pear, 237
Pilaf, nutted, 217
Pineapple:
    carrot juice, 31
    date bar cookies, 231
    pick me up, 31
    slaw, 106
Piquant sauce, summer squash with, 194
Pita:
    quick splits, 90
    splits, 89
Pizza:
    potato and arugula, 85
    verde, 84
Polenta, bean, 201
Polish Beets, 182
Poppy Seed Dressing, lime, 112
Potato(es):
    baked with leeks, 188
    languedoc, 189
    mashed with turnips, 187
    new, duxelle, 187